To Lou, for all his patience, strength and love.

NO-ONE SHOULD ATTEMPT WITHDRAWAL FROM ANY PRESCRIBED MEDICINES WITHOUT SEEKING MEDICAL ADVICE.

The names of the members of the medical profession and establishments in this book are fictitious. Any resemblance to any person or place with the same name is purely coincidental.

First published in 1990 by Headway Books
4 West Moor Lane, Heslington, York, England.

© Heather Jones and Headway Books, 1990

ISBN 0 9513945 2 6

Typeset by Saxon Printing Ltd., Saxon House, Heritage Gate, Derby.

FOREWORD

This touching account, so simply and straightforwardly told, grips like a novel, yet is a true story. It will catch at the hearts of all who care to read it through. In particular, many among the several millions of tranquilliser users in the world will recognise themselves in Heather's honest record of her own experiences.

As one who has seen many individuals through the personal struggles of tranquilliser withdrawal, with all its attendant effects on husbands, wives, children, friends and relations, I can vouch that Heather's story is absolutely genuine and typical. One can only admire Heather's courage and hope, which sustained her in the search for her own solution. She will inspire others to find their own drug-free ways of coping with the stresses of modern life.

Dr. Heather Ashton,
Consultant in Clinical Pharmacology,
The University,
Newcastle upon Tyne,
England.

INTRODUCTION

Five years have now passed since I last took a tranquilliser.

During those black early days of withdrawal I believe I went to hell and back: learning to live without the aid of an addictive drug is probably one of the hardest lessons the body will ever have to learn.

As the months passed by, many of the distressing symptoms began to slowly disappear. The colic and digestive disturbances proved particularly persistent – these are now being treated with acupuncture, anti-fungal drugs, diet and vitamin supplements.

Coping with tension and anxiety without the crutch of the tranquillisers proved to be an especially difficult task. Muscle stiffness and pain, especially in the neck and shoulders, seems to be a great problem with many people, and I believe deep breathing, relaxation exercises and even hypnotherapy can be of special benefit. It is necessary to learn to relax again, as the body has forgotten how and needs teaching properly.

Many people become agoraphobic during withdrawal and when this is accompanied by deep depression, the sufferers can become, understandably, discouraged: they can begin to feel as though they'll never 'make it'. However it is very important to recognise that both of these symptoms are temporary: as the nervous system becomes stronger they, too, will disappear along with the others.

Coming to terms with life-long problems without the ana-esthetic of pills, and having to 'live through' events and experiences that were once blinded by drugs, can be traumatic.

Many people find that they become old – especially when they have taken the drug for a long time – and grieve for the lost years. During the first weeks of withdrawal, people sometimes wonder who they are and may find it hard to recognise this new person. They often feel guilty and confused.

This is why I am so pleased to see more support groups starting up around the country. They are invaluable in helping the sufferer to cope with his experiences as, without the proper guidance and support, withdrawal can be an immensely frightening and distressing experience.

I would like to see more help from G.P.s; fortunately many now realise that tranquillisers are addictive and recognise withdrawal symptoms, but it is important for them to explain to a sufferer that full recovery can, in some cases, take many months. For patients to believe that withdrawal takes just a few weeks means they will become depressed and disheartened when the symptoms persist.

I would also like to see more help from the NHS: specifically, hospital treatment coming from Pharmacological Units rather than from Psychiatric Departments; professional help for the learning of relaxation, including physiotherapy and hypnosis, together with expert guidance for yoga classes, swimming and general aerobics. I found the latter extremely beneficial as, in common with all exercise, it not only strengthens the heart and lungs and helps supply your body with oxygen, but also heightens the immune system and helps eliminate toxic wastes and chemicals from the system. I also believe a physchotherapist should be available for those who find emerging from withdrawal a harrowing experience.

Someone once wrote "Tranquillisers are the Anaesthetics of the Emotions". This is true and, although, when used properly, they have an application in modern medicine, it is the experience of myself and of millions of others that, taken over a long time, they poison the body and destroy the mind.

I was first prescribed tranquillisers to help me cope with my baby son's sleeplessness – a son who has now grown into a fine young man, but who is still nocturnal and thinks his nights should be days! Time hasn't changed this and neither, regrettably, has it altered the opinion of many doctors who still prescribe tranquillisers on a long-term basis. It is my belief, however, that in time, Benzodiazepine Withdrawal will be an illness of the past.

Until that happy day, in order to alleviate the suffering of others, those of us who are further along the same road of recovery will be able to help – where possible – by listening and reassuring them that they *will* recover and be able to lead a full and rewarding life once more.

> *Heather Jones,*
> *July, 1988*

Heather Jones was born in Wolverhampton but spent most of her early life in Kingston-upon-Hull. At school she developed a keen interest in writing and English literature. In 1964 she joined the W.R.A.F. and was stationed at Royal Air Force Patrington, near Withernsea, and it was there that she met and married her husband, Lou.

In 1967 they moved to Newcastle-on-Tyne, where they have lived ever since with their two children.

1971 – 1976

"Try these – once to twice daily, they'll do the trick." The doctor pushed the prescription across his big mahogany desk.

"Please can you help?" I had asked. My baby son had decided he was nocturnal, and if he wasn't tired and irritable, he was certainly making me so! In addition to sleeplessness, I had a young daughter to look after during the day, so I had come to the doctor thinking I needed a tonic.

"I don't think so," he had replied to my suggestion, "these will make you feel better."

I looked at the piece of paper he had handed me and read the word *Valium* for the first time. "Don't worry," his voice was reassuring, "they won't do you any harm; you can take them all your life if you wish."

* * * * *

For the next two years I took Valium as he had prescribed and felt fine. 1973 was a good year. My husband gained promotion and moved into a new house. My good friend Eileen's first baby was born and Sunderland won the cup! I made another good friend – Joan – and, as the months flew by, my life became a social whirl. Any problems that did crop up could swiftly be wiped out by taking a Valium. Life was pretty good and another year went by.

"I really think it is time to change doctors," I said to my husband, Lou, one day. "We have been in this house for over a year now and a new surgery has just opened up the road. Let's face it, it will be a lot handier and it will save all that travelling."

He nodded in agreement. "Anything you want, love," and seemed unconcerned one way or the other. In those days his mind and time were always preoccupied with his career. I didn't mind. I had my new house, two lovely children, a regular night out with the girls and, as always, when needed, my little yellow pills. I felt very relaxed and content with my lot.

However changing doctors brought a new problem. "I'm sorry you will have to see the doctor about that," the receptionist smiled pleasantly. I had just asked for a repeat prescription, something which I had been doing regularly at my other doctor's for years; I didn't see any problem in having the same agreement with this new doctor.

"That's all right, could I make an appointment, please?"

"If you'd like to hang on for five minutes I can fit you in between patients." I agreed and settled myself down with a magazine, but it wasn't long before the bell rang. "Your turn, Mrs Jones," the receptionist handed me my file, "the door at the end of the corridor."

The doctor, plump and fresh-faced, was younger than I imagined. "What can I do for you?" Her smile was friendly.

"I'd like a repeat prescription for some more Valium please." I shuffled rather uneasily in my chair. She put her pen down and looked at me.

"How long have you been taking them for?"

"On and off for about three years."

"For what reason?" she asked. "Oh, my son wouldn't sleep and I was very tired and irritable – run down, you would say – and as vitamins didn't help, my last doctor prescribed Valium."

"Does your son sleep now?"

"Yes, he's a lot better. He's still something of a night owl, but school tends to tire him out, thank goodness."

"Well how about cutting them down? Three years is far too long, you know."

It seemed like a sensible idea so I agreed with her and began to reduce the tablets. I can honestly say I felt no ill effects. It was Christmas 1974 and I had cut down the tablets over a period of three weeks – quicker than the doctor had recommended – but

I suspected I was pregnant, and the thought of taking pills during pregnancy worried me.

Two weeks after taking the last dose I suffered a miscarriage, and was admitted to hospital for a routine operation. The anaesthetic that was used was a high dose of Valium. For three days after that I couldn't have cared if the house had burned down!

*   *   *   *   *

It was January 1975, and losing the baby had affected me more deeply than I thought it would; a couple of other things had happened to upset me and I was feeling pretty low. Unfortunately, unlike in the past, this time I did not have any pills to cover it up; I paid a visit to the doctor in tears.

"I think you should go back onto Valium for the time being. Maybe a slightly higher dose than before." She smiled sympathetically.

Although life could not be described as being exactly rosy on this new dosage, at least it was bearable and I again felt able to cope. However as the months passed by, my problems did not go away as they had done in the early days on the pills – in fact, they had begun to appear greater in some respects than before.

My friend Eileen had moved south and I became very close to Joan – who was proving to be an understanding friend. My husband had become involved with his work and spent many evenings in town, sometimes not coming home until the early hours; I would sit and wait for him, worried and anxious, sometimes taking an extra Valium to help me get through the long hours of the night.

They became my little yellow friends. Always there when needed.

*   *   *   *   *

It was during the long hot summer of 1976 that I first noticed my personality had begun to change. I started to become withdrawn and insecure; suffering bouts of depression together with uncontrollable outbursts of rage which had a dire effect on my family and friends. Some days I was impossible to live with because of my terrific mood swings and once, while on a caravanning holiday with the family, my husband Lou made the mistake of forgetting to put one of the suitcases in the car. You would have thought he had signed the declaration for the start of World War Three!

"You can just drive back and get it!" I screamed at him. The fact that Newcastle, where we lived, was over two hundred miles away, did not seem to matter at all.

"I can't do that," he replied, his dark eyes begging me not to go on.

"Well get out then," I said, "until you *can* do something!" I shook with uncontrollable fury. The children watched us, wide-eyed and silent; they were accustomed to these outbursts now, but somehow never seemed able to accept them.

"Don't you dare move!" I glared at the children, and they stared back, transfixed; their small faces pale and serious.

It was not long before Lou returned, his tall slim frame exaggerated by the smallness of the caravan. "I've rung Joan and she is going to send the case down by rail. All we have to do is get someone to pick it up."

I still wasn't pleased. "You are stupid – you really are!"

He rarely defended himself when I was in these moods but, as I sat down angrily, the feeling of resentment gradually began to fade. "God, what am I doing? I don't want to be like this. I wish I could tell him I don't mean to say those things," I thought to myself. But somehow I couldn't say the words.

I promised myself I would try and make it up to him in other ways and I would try harder to curb these temper outbursts. But I was beginning to realise that deep down it was a promise I would not be able to keep.

My mood swings became more apparent as the months went by. But somehow, even though I couldn't cope with the conflict in my own life, I found I could help other people with their problems, and was pleased when they brought them to me. It was because of this that I joined a voluntary organisation, hoping that by listening to other people's troubles, mine would seem insignificant in comparison. I enjoyed this work tremendously, and stayed for nearly two years until something else cropped up that took me completely by surprise...

I don't know when agoraphobia actually began. It seemed to creep in surreptitiously and I would put it down to feeling 'under the weather' or that places and shops were either too hot or too full. I remember that someone once told me that I was becoming an agoraphobic and I laughed it off. "Who me? You must be joking! I'm the one with bags of confidence and can go anywhere on my own. No – this is something else – probably my hormones or something. It'll go away if I try not to think about it."

I couldn't have been more wrong.

"I don't think I can make it tonight," I told my friend Joan. We were about to go out for the evening.

"Well, see how you feel later," she said, and I nodded but knew that this feeling of uneasiness in public places would still be there no matter how much later it was.

I had started to make excuses in order just to keep from going out. If excuses didn't work, an extra Valium would be the answer and somehow I would cope. They had become a necessary part of my life now; where I went, they went. "I need them," I thought, "the doctors say they are harmless, so there is no problem."

I was now taking 15 mg a day, plus any extras that were needed when I had to face stressful situations. However these were becoming more and more frequent, and every day minor obstacles were becoming major hurdles. The monthly visits to the doctor for repeat prescriptions were getting closer together.

"I just don't feel like they're helping any more," I told the doctor. "I just feel so anxious and depressed all the time."

"How long have you felt like this?" He was a new doctor in the practice.

"It's sort of built up over the months," I replied, "I don't seem to be able to cope with stress very well. And another thing is I'm always so very tired all the time."

"How do you sleep? O.K?"

"Not exactly. I don't have any problem getting to sleep, but I wake up in the middle of the night, usually at about three o'clock."

"That's probably because the drugs aren't working any more," he said. "I am going to give you something to take at night."

I was instantly on guard: these would be sleeping pills – and I wasn't so sure I wanted them. "I don't want to feel drugged the next day," I told him.

"Don't worry," he assured me, "these won't give you any 'hangover' feelings – they are very mild." And he handed me a subscription for Tranxene, another form of tranquilliser. I was to take one at night, every night, for a month.

Life had become very flat now. I felt void of all emotions and everything seemed to be happening on one level. I went about my daily duties as before, but without any feeling; I felt as though emotionally I had turned into a robot.

I finished the course of Tranxene, but two days after taking the last tablet, I experienced one of the most frightening symptoms I had ever known since taking the pills. My children, Louise and Paul, had just left for school when I began to experience a tremendous panic sensation that started in the bottom of my stomach and crept upwards into my head. My legs turned to jelly, my heart pounded, but worst of all, I felt a fear I had never known before. "I'll have to speak to someone," I thought. I picked up the telephone and dialled my husband's work telephone number.

"May I speak to Mr. Jones please?" My knuckles were white as I gripped the receiver. I heard the receptionist call his name over the intercom and, although he must have come to the phone within minutes, it seemed like hours.

"Hello love," his voice seemed to quell my panic slightly.

"I feel so ill," I told him, "and I don't know what to do!"

"What sort of ill?"

"I don't know," I replied frantically, "faint and weak and I can't stand up properly. I feel like I'm going to die. It's just awful."

"Do you think you have caught something?" He sounded concerned, and I began to cry.

"*No!* It's not like that! It's, it's...oh! – I don't know *what* it's like! It's just awful and I'm so frightened. Please, I want you to come home. *Please* can you Lou - *please?*" The waves of panic were really beginning to surge through me now.

"I can't do that, love," he answered, "we're short-staffed today. Do you want me to get the doctor?"

"I don't know. I just feel so ill and I don't want to be on my own."

"Give me the number of the surgery and I'll give them a ring. In the meantime make yourself a cup of tea and take it easy. O.K?"

It seemed that hours passed before the doctor arrived – but it was just ten o'clock when I heard the doorbell ring. "What seems to be the matter?" he asked, as we entered the sitting-room.

"All of a sudden I felt really ill," I answered, sinking onto the settee. "My whole body is shaking inside and I feel so frightened; my heart feels like it is coming out of my chest!" The tears began to pour down my face.

"I'll just take your blood pressure," he said sitting down next to me. He seemed concerned when he unfolded the green strapping from my arm. "Hmm! It's up a bit and your pulse is quite fast. Have you finished the tablets I prescribed to you?"

"Yes a couple of days ago."

"How many Valium are you taking a day now?"

"I was on three a day, but I cut them down whilst I was taking the others, as I didn't want to take too many..."

"I think you had better up the dose again," he interrupted quietly, "and I would like you to see a doctor at the hospital." Something in his tone made me cautious.

"What sort of doctor?" I asked.

"It would be a psychiatrist."

I felt too ill to show a reaction or to argue, but inside I was deeply shocked. A psychiatrist? Surely it hadn't come to this! But the doctor continued talking. "I think you probably don't feel up to going to the hospital at the moment, but the doctor can come here to see you, if you want." He closed his case and stood up. "In the meantime though, I want you to go back onto the Valium. Do you have enough?"

"I...no, I don't think so." I mumbled. I didn't know whether I had or not, but it was easier to say I hadn't. I was still too stunned to argue. He handed me a prescription, told me not to worry and left.

After he had gone, I made another cup of tea and, still shaken, took a Valium. The effect was miraculous – it was as though someone had waved a magic wand – and within fifteen minutes all fear and panic abated. Suddenly the telephone rang. It was the nurse from the doctor's surgery.

"Can you make sure you will be in this afternoon as there is a Dr. Dawson from the Western General Hospital coming to see you. It'll be around two o'clock. Is that all right?"

I felt a great deal better after the Valium, but I didn't like to say I wasn't so sure I needed one now, so I agreed. Besides, the awful feeling of panic might return. Better be safe than sorry, I thought.

Dr. Dawson was a tiny, unobtrusive sort of man, with a shock of silver grey hair and eyes that twinkled from behind dark-rimmed spectacles. I immediately felt at ease with him and showed him into the lounge where he sat down, opened his briefcase and took out his notebook and pen.

"Your G.P. rang me and told me you were in a very anxious state and might need help." He smiled at me over his glasses.

"I don't feel so bad now," I made an effort to smile back, "but I felt awful this morning. I was sweating and shaking all over and my heart was thumping so fast I thought it was going to come out of my chest. I thought I was going to die, I really did!" I began to twist my fingers backwards and forwards.

"How do you feel now?" he asked.

"Oh, a lot better. Just very tired and depressed." I noticed his eyes fall to my hands.

"When did those feelings you mentioned go away?"

I thought for a few seconds. "I think it was after I took a Valium. Yes, that's right, everything seemed to calm down inside after that." I nodded as though agreeing with myself.

"*Had* you stopped taking them?"

"Not quite," I said, "I had just cut them right down because I had been given Tranxene to take at night and I don't like taking too many pills." He looked at me for a few moments and then started to write in his notebook.

"How many do you take now?" He carried on writing as he spoke.

"I did take three 5 mg a day."

I watched him as he carried on scribbling. "Are you sleeping all right now?" he asked.

"I was while I was taking Tranxene," I answered, "but before that I used to wake up in the middle of the night and couldn't get back to sleep until just before it was time to get up."

"Hmm, I see," he said. "I think you had better carry on with the 15 mg of Valium for a while, they're obviously what you need." He had stopped writing and was putting the top on his pen.

"Those awful feelings though, what were they?"

"What you described are classic anxiety symptoms."

"They're nothing to do with stopping the Tranxene then?"

"Well, in a way, yes. The Tranxene was obviously helping your anxiety, so when you stopped them you would automatically feel worse."

I wasn't convinced. "But I never felt like that before I took them," I told him.

"Yes – I know," he answered with a smile, "but you were taking Valium then, weren't you? They would control all those symptoms you mention."

But I was still uncertain. "I can't remember *ever* feeling like that – even before I was given Valium. In fact, when I think back, I wasn't really very anxious at all – just a little bit tired and irritable." He looked at me kindly and leaned forward to speak.

"Well, you probably have more reason to be anxious now – maybe you have more problems now than you did before?"

I thought for a few moments. Did I have more problems? Perhaps he was right – maybe I did. "And you think that is what is wrong with me?"

"Well, I definitely think you are suffering from anxiety and depression, and your doctor said you were very distressed and needed psychological help. And while I must admit that you are not as bad as I thought you would be, even so, I would still like to see you again. Do you think you could come down to the out-patient department at the hospital?"

I wasn't very sure. "Do you think it will help?"

"I'm sure it will," he replied. "We will have a lot longer to discuss your problems there. My secretary will write to you with an appointment." He closed his notebook, put it back in his briefcase, and snapped it shut.

"How long will that take to arrange?" If I was going to attend a psychiatric clinic I wanted to get the visits over and done with as soon as possible.

"Maybe a week to ten days, it shouldn't be long," he said, standing up as he answered.

I thanked him for coming and showed him to the door. "I'll see you again very soon," he said. "In the meantime carry on taking the Valium as before."

He smiled and left.

1977

Two weeks to the day of Dr Dawson's home visit, Lou and I were sitting in the waiting room of the Psychological Outpatients Unit. It was situated at the end of the main hospital outpatients' department, and consisted of a reception desk and a long corridor with many doors opening on to it. It was opposite one of these doors that the waiting area was provided; a sort of recess in the wall with bench seats arranged around it.

Apart from Lou and I there were only three other people waiting. Directly opposite was a young girl of about eighteen, sitting with an older woman who seemed to be her mother; she seemed very agitated and not at all interested in the bright conversation her companion was trying to make. On the bench facing the corridor sat an old man dressed in a shabby overcoat. He rarely lifted his head, but just stared at the smoke which rose from a cigarette he held cupped in his upturned hand.

A table piled high with old magazines separated us from the other three. Lou picked one up and started to read. "I wish he would talk to me instead," I said to myself, but that was something he did very rarely these days. The door opened directly opposite and Dr. Dawson popped his head round.

"Mrs. Jones – would you like to come in please?" he said, and I followed him into his room.

Once inside, I was surprised how cheerful it was compared to the corridor outside: bright, chintzy curtains hung at the window and a huge vase of chrysanthemums sat on a bookcase in the corner of the room opposite the door. The sun streamed onto his desk and I noticed how much taller Dr. Dawson seemed as he took his seat behind it.

"How are you doing?" He gave me a warm smile.

"I feel O.K." I answered, "but some days are worse than others. I still can't cope with stress very well, and I feel very washed out and tired."

"When did you *start* feeling like this? Can you remember?" His smile was reassuring, and I thought for a few moments before answering.

"It was a gradual process. Maybe a couple of years ago things started to go wrong. But not all of a sudden, though. I think my sleep was the first thing I noticed that changed. I used to have no problems at all at night, in fact I used to boast that I could sleep on a clothes-line if need be! Now I wake up after about three or four hours and lie there wide awake but exhausted until about seven o'clock."

He picked up his pen and began to write in a large, orange-coloured file.

"It isn't like ordinary insomnia," I continued. "I don't have any trouble in getting to sleep. I just can't help waking up in the night, usually at about three o'clock. It doesn't matter how much I tire myself out the day before. I seem to have tried everything possible – yoga, long walks, warm milky drinks – but nothing seems to work, and I always wake in the middle of the night."

"It is a *form* of insomnia," he had stopped writing, "and it is also a very common one. It's usually a symptom of depression – what we call *endogenous* depression."

I had never heard the term before. "What is that?" I asked.

"Endogenous means 'from within' and it describes a depression in which, as in your case, the cause is not an obvious one. It is usually something that is deep-rooted, probably going back a long way."

I was still very puzzled. "And this is what you think is the matter with me?"

He smiled. "More than likely, but it is only part of the story. You are also suffering from anxiety and that's what we are going to try and get to the bottom of." He sat back in his chair and looked at me kindly. "You say that your anxiety started a while ago. Can you think of anything that happened that might for a moment have triggered it off?"

I thought for a while before answering. "Not that I can think of. I was quite depressed about two years ago – I had a lot on my plate – but I have sorted all that out now. Anyway, you say that my problems are probably deep-rooted and those weren't especially."

His tone became suddenly matter of fact. "How do you and your husband get on?"

I tried to think of some concrete reason to explain the way in which the relationship between Lou and myself had deteriorated. "We had some problems recently," I said, "he used to go out a lot straight from work, and even though I knew where he was, I used to worry terribly, wondering if he'd had an accident."

"You say he doesn't do this any more?"

"Yes, that's right."

"But you obviously still worry, though?" he asked, smiling kindly.

"I try not to," I replied, "but I suppose it is always there at the back of my mind."

"That's understandable," he peered at me from over his glasses, "and continuous worry all adds to the anxiety you are experiencing."

"But surely this can't be the reason I feel so tense and tired all the time? I mean, I've had lots of problems throughout my life, bigger than this, and I've always managed to bounce back!"

"Maybe so," he replied, "but this will be contributing to it, and of course when you are younger...you have that little bit of extra resilience, don't you?" He paused for a moment, and glanced at my file. "Let me see, how old are you? Hmm, just turned thirty-four." He tapped his pen on the desk and thought for a few seconds. He then began to write again without looking up. "How many children do you have?"

"Two," I replied. "Louise is nearly thirteen and Paul is nine."

He put his pen down and rested his chin in his hand. "Were they normal pregnancies? You didn't have any problems...especially *after* they were born?"

"I had threatened miscarriages with both," I answered, "and Louise was a breech delivery, but apart from that – no, everything was fine."

"No post-natal depression?"

"No – I don't think so. Just a few tears when they were a few days old, but that's normal isn't it?" He didn't answer, but started to write again.

I looked about the small room and suddenly felt very confused. How were these questions related to anxiety? It didn't seem to make sense. I had been well and healthy after my children were born and had suffered with no depression at all.

"You say you nearly miscarried with both babies – was there a reason for this?" he asked.

"I don't think so. I'm prone to them I believe."

"Oh," he said, "why do you say that?"

"Well, I lost a baby before Louise was born, and two more after Paul."

"Did they give you a reason for this?"

"How do you mean? What sort of reason?"

"Well sometimes the problem can be a hormone deficiency. Progesterone – or rather a lack of it – can cause all sorts of problems: miscarriages, pre-menstrual tension, anxiety, to name but a few. I think with your history there is a good chance you might be deficient and I'd like you to go on a course for a month and see if there is any improvement in your anxiety. Also I'm going to give you an anti-depressant that will help you to sleep properly again."

"I don't really like taking pills," I told him.

"It's only for a short while, so don't worry," he reassured me.

"Will I have to stop Valium again?" I asked.

"No, it's O.K. to take the two together; they don't react with each other." He reached for his prescription pad. "I'd like you to come back in a month to see how you are getting on."

I smiled and stood up.

"Make an appointment with the receptionist." He handed me the prescription and smiled warmly back. I thanked him and left.

"At last," I thought, "I'm going to feel alright again soon."

The monthly visits to the psychiatrist soon became a part of my life, but the improvement I had hoped for did not happen. The first anti-depressant, Imipramine, had made me feel dreadful – dizzy, off-balance and very dry-mouthed. "They are probably too strong for you," Dr. Dawson had said, prescribing a smaller dose. But these, too, had had the same effects as the first, so I stopped taking them after just a few days.

It was now my third visit to see Dr Dawson.

"I had to stop them," I told him, "I felt exactly the same on them as I did on the higher dose. I had no co-ordination and felt light-headed and dizzy all the time."

"And how is the depression?"

"Oh, that's O.K." I shrugged. "Some days I'm alright and then 'wham!' Everything goes to pieces and I can't cope with the smallest problem. Also, I seem to get upset very easily, especially with people I am close to and care about, flying off the handle at the least little thing."

"Most of us lose our temper at some time or other for seemingly very little reason," he remarked.

"I know. But this is not like a normal temper outburst. I can feel quite murderous and sometimes lash out at anything. I know I'm being irrational but I can't seem to stop it."

"Have you always had a temper?"

"Well, yes – I've always been quick to lose my temper. But then I've always been quick to calm down again, too. This is different. It's like I'm a different person."

"Hmm, I see." He pondered for a while, tapping his pen on the desk. "These outbursts, do they coincide with your monthly cycle? That is, are they worse near the end rather than at the beginning?"

My answer was very vague. "I don't know. Well, yes...maybe they do sometimes. I've not really taken much notice, so I'm not really sure."

"Did you get any benefit at all from the Progesterone?" he asked.

"Well – I've put weight on," I smiled, "but that's about all."

"And how are you sleeping?"

"No better," I replied, "I still wake up in the middle of the night."

Dr. Dawson thought before answering. "I see," he said, "well as I have already told you, this is usually a sign of depression...but it could also mean that the Valium is no longer strong enough..."

I didn't let him finish. Not *strong* enough? I was already taking two different tablets a day – where would it end? "I don't want to up the dose any higher," I interrupted.

But again, he gave me a reassuring smile. "You don't have to," he continued. "I'd like you to try a very mild sedative to take at night. You can carry on taking the Valium as well as they're both from the same family of drugs: Benzodiazepines. These are called Nitrazepam, or you might know them better as Mogadon." He was right – the name was familiar. "See if they help. Take one a night to start off with. and carry on with the Valium. One 5 mg tablet three times a day, wasn't it?" He had begun to write out a prescription.

As he handed me the yellow form I stood up to leave. "Let's hope these help," he said and, yet again, I thanked him and left.

"Are these the answer?" I thought to myself, as I walked down the hospital corridor. Deep down I had a feeling that, yet again, they wouldn't be – but what else could I do? He was the doctor...surely he knew best?

*   *   *   *   *

I took the Mogadon as prescribed and slept soundly at night. Valium kept me going through the day and life became bearable once more. No more aggression or anxiety. No more fear. I remembered these feelings were very similar to those when I took Tranxene but, despite the fact that I could cope once more, I wasn't very happy. *Something* wasn't right.

"I don't want to feel like this," I told my G.P.

"Feel like what?" she asked.

"Sort of flat and dead," I replied.

"Do you feel drugged in any way?"

"No, not really," I answered, "but to be honest I don't think I feel anything at all." That was what was bothering me. This dead, unemotional feeling.

"You must feel something," she remarked.

"No, I don't – honestly. It's as though I'm numb all over. Do I really have to take the two lots of drugs?" I was trying hard to convince her as I wasn't sure she believed what I was saying; she leaned back on her chair and frowned at me slightly.

"Dr. Dawson prescribed these drugs for you to take you know. He wouldn't have done so if he didn't think they were necessary. He is a consultant psychiatrist and knows what he is talking about." Her voice had a slightly irritable edge.

"I know" I replied, "but I still don't like taking sleeping tablets, so...I think I'll stop taking them for a while."

"That is entirely up to you," she returned coldly, and leaned forward in her chair adopting the tone of a teacher towards a naughty child. "You know we sent you to a top psychiatrist only because we thought he could help you, and a lot of time and money has been spent in so doing. If you are going to keep on refusing his treatment he is not going to be very happy about it."

I didn't like her attitude, and for a few seconds felt the urge to tell her so. But I bit my lip and said nothing: I had come here determined to stand my ground. "I know a lot of time and money has been spent on me, but I still think I'll drop the Mogadon. I'd like to see how I get on without them."

I could tell immediately by her face that I had said the wrong thing. But deep down I felt that my decision was right, so I left her surgery determined to stop taking Mogadon.

And this is what I did. However contrary to what I had hoped for and expected, almost immediately things began to get very much worse. I became irritable and morose and took my black moods out on my husband and children. I would spend my time worrying and fretting over everyday problems which seemed to be becoming increasingly more difficult to solve. Sleep was no longer a welcome relief; I would lie awake in the middle of the night, soaked in perspiration and feeling terribly afraid. My confidence had now begun to disappear, and my fear of public places was becoming impossible to conceal.

"Where do you fancy going tonight?" Joan had rung to make arrangements for a night out.

"Can we go just for a drive and maybe a drink in a country pub?" I suggested.

"We are the only people I know who travel twenty miles just for one bitter lemon!" she said with a laugh.

A few months ago I would have enjoyed these nights out, but now, the fear that accompanied them and any other journey away from home, was becoming harder and harder to fight. Wherever I went I would always be counting the minutes, willing them to pass quickly so I could go back to the safety of my home.

It was about this time that the voluntary work that I had found so rewarding suddenly became too much to cope with. When it was my turn to be on duty, I would ring up with an excuse not to go in, which made me feel guilty and ashamed: I loved my work and hated letting people down.

I knew I was no longer the extrovert, happy person I used to be; I was becoming interested in only two things – myself and my illness.

"I can't understand it," I told Dr. Dawson on one of my monthly visits, "I still feel so anxious all the time and I don't know why. I mean I'm taking Valium, aren't I? Shouldn't that make things better?"

"You've been taking them for quite a while now, haven't you?" he asked.

"Six years, I think."

"Well, I think you are probably becoming used to the amount that you are taking. However rather than putting the dose up, I'd like to try another form of tranquilliser. This one is called Melleril – a *major* one – Valium is what we call a *minor* tranquilliser."

Yet again I left his clinic with a new prescription, and a new sense of hope. But it took me just one week of taking this new drug he had prescribed to realise that Melleril wasn't the answer! If there was any slight improvement in the anxiety, this was overshadowed by the other symptoms the drug induced: I experienced dizziness and faintness but, worst of all, all my muscles began to jerk and twitch uncontrollably.

"I will have to go and see the G.P." I told Lou, "but I am frightened in case she gets annoyed with me like she did the last time."

"Well surely there must be another one at the surgery you can see?" he suggested. I had heard there was a new lady doctor who had just joined the practice who was very pleasant and understanding.

"Yes there is a new one," I said to him. "I'll try and get an appointment to see her." But I had one more request. "When I go," I asked him, "will you come with me? I don't want to go on my own."

He looked at me and smiled. He knew by my face I was anxious and nervous. "Don't worry love," he reassured me, "I'll come with you."

"Mr. and Mrs. Jones isn't it?" The new doctor smiled at Lou and I, and beckoned us to sit down.

She was a small slim figure dressed in a beige tweed suit with a pretty cream blouse underneath. There was a small cameo brooch pinned in the middle of the collar, and her fair hair was swept up into a soft bun with tendrils which dangled down around her neck. I noticed she wore no make-up.

"Well, what can I do for you?" she asked kindly.

"I'm seeing Dr. Dawson from the Western General at the moment," I said, "he's been treating me for anxiety and depression." I looked across to Lou as though for reassurance. "It's just that I don't seem to be getting any better. He keeps giving me different anti-depressants and hypnotics, but these don't help at all. In fact they make me feel worse."

"What are you taking now?" she asked.

"He put me on Melleril a couple of weeks ago and they're making me feel dreadful. Are you supposed to feel like this?"

"I don't know, it depends how you feel," she replied with a smile.

"Well I'm dizzy all the time; my balance seems to be affected, and I'm jumping and jerking all over the place. It's difficult to explain but I definitely don't feel right."

"I see," she frowned slightly. "Tell me, are you still taking Valium?"

"No," I replied, "but I definitely felt better on them than I do with these new ones."

She looked through my file for a few moments before she spoke again. "Personally I don't think you need all these drugs, but I see Dr Dawson thinks differently." I was pleased she thought this and I knew Lou was too.

"It's just that when my wife was last here, she was told in no uncertain terms that Dr. Dawson's advice was the best to be had, and if she didn't do as he said, he wouldn't be at all pleased," he remarked.

"If you don't feel happy taking these drugs, you don't have to," she said shaking her head.

"I'm pleased that you think like that," I told her. "It's just that I don't want to be regarded as being difficult."

"Rubbish!" she retorted. "It's your body and it's up to you what you put into it. If you have any problems come and see me and I'll see what I can do. Now let me see – when do you see Dr. Dawson again?" She looked at the letter that was attached to my file.

"Not for about two weeks," I told her.

"Well, in that case, I suggest you telephone him and tell him how you feel and see what he has to say. In the meantime I'll have a word with my partner about you and see what we can come up with. As I said before, I'm sure drugs aren't the answer, but because she is your doctor, I'll have to ask her opinion first."

For the first time in months I felt as though I had achieved something at last, but this feeling of success was to be very short-lived.

The next day I spoke to Dr. Dawson on the phone. "Stop the Melleril," he told me, "and go back onto Valium. In the meantime I'll send you a prescription for something else."

The something else turned out to be another anti-depressant which I had to take with Valium....

*   *   *   *   *

My life was now revolving around pills, but instead of feeling any better, my fears and anxieties were becoming greater. The monthly trips to the psychiatrist would normally end with my being prescribed a different anti-depressant or hypnotic and, as always, a repeat prescription for the only things that seemed to keep me going: my little yellow friends. Valium was the only drug that didn't seem to produce any of the unpleasant side-effects that came from the other pills.

I had them everywhere – little brown bottles with just six or seven left – they were in handbags I rarely used, bedroom cabinets and kitchen cupboards, and in pockets of nearly every coat or jacket I owned. I praised their virtues to my family and friends, recommending them for all types of stressful situations that they found difficult to handle.

It was around this time that we made tactful enquiries as to what steps had to be taken in order to change your G.P. within the practice. The receptionist was very helpful and informed us that this would not be necessary. "Just try and come when the doctor you prefer is on duty," she explained in a pleasant manner, "there is no need to change doctors."

But within a week we received a letter.

"It is from the General Practitioners Committee," Lou said as he opened the envelope. "Apparently it seems our relationship with our doctor has broken down and we have been requested to find another."

I was devastated. I felt as though it was a direct personal snub.

"Don't get upset," Lou said, trying to comfort me. "It's for the best. You know we weren't very keen on her anyway."

"It'll be ever so hard to find another one," I cried.

"Course it won't," he said reassuringly, "we'll get one. It'll be no problem, you wait and see."

He was right – we found one two days later. There were three doctors in this practice and it was the senior one, Dr. Scott, we saw at the interview. The first impression I had of her, was that of a straight-laced school-teacher, and she made only a vague reference to Dr Dawson.

Because she never questioned the monthly visits to the hospital, I never mentioned them either. I didn't want to upset anybody again so I knew I would have to accept them as part of my life. And so the prescription for Valium continued and, at the same time, the inexorable deterioration of my physical and mental health.

1978

"There must be something seriously wrong with me mentally. I just *know* there is," I would say to myself. Some days I would feel as though I was going out of my mind as my moods swung from extreme 'highs' to deep black despair.

I became extremely paranoid, believing that it was 'me against the world' – and thinking the world to be a place full of anxieties and fears. The fear was like nothing else I'd ever known before – it had crept up on me slowly, without giving any warning – and the mild agoraphobia I had experienced at first was now becoming more and more obvious: I would do *anything* not be on my own, and going out had become a major – if not impossible – task.

School holidays were a godsend. Whereas most mothers looked forward to their children going back to school, I dreaded it. I would spend hours on the telephone talking to anyone who had the time to listen and, if my friends weren't available, I'd ring Lou.

"It doesn't matter how busy you are, I cried down the phone, "I have to speak to somebody." I could only think about myself and my fear.

"Can't you ring Joan?" he suggested. "Maybe she'll come round for a coffee."

"I can't, she's at work today."

"What about Eileen then?" Eileen had recently moved back home after living two years in the South.

"I can't! She has an ante-natal appointment at the hospital! Please, I'm so frightened – I just don't want to be on my own." I knew it was unreasonable to telephone him like this at work, but my fear was greater than any reasoning.

Lou tried to reason with me. "Well, what can I do?" He sounded slightly put out.

"I don't know," I replied frantically, "but please don't let me be on my own." There was silence on the end of the phone. "Are you still there?" I cried.

"Yes. But as I've just said, what do you want me to do?"

"Have you had your lunch yet?" I asked him.

"No, not yet," he replied. His voice had a cautious tone. "Why do you ask?"

"Can you come home then?" I asked hopefully, "I'll cook you something."

"I haven't really got the time..." He sounded as though he was going to refuse.

"Oh *please!*" I cried. "I don't know what I'll do if you don't." He paused for a few moments before answering.

"I'll see what I can do," he said, "but I can't promise anything."

I spent the next hour pacing up and down, trying hard to quell the awful fear. Many times during my life I had been on my own – lived on my own, even – and I had always regarded myself as being totally independent. "What is wrong with me?" I asked myself wringing my hands, my heart pounding like a drum. "*Why* am I like this?" It was a question I couldn't answer, a feeling I didn't understand.

Before too long Lou arrived home. His mood appeared to be a mixture of agitation and worry. "I can't stop long, love," he said, putting his car keys on the table. I looked at him, panic building up again inside.

"I'm so frightened all the time," I said, "and I don't really know why. I remember being like this about a year ago – do you remember – when I stopped taking Tranxene and had to cut the Valium right down?"

"Have you been cutting the Valium down again?" he asked, sitting down in an easy chair.

"No," I replied, "but I'm sure the amount I'm taking isn't strong enough any more. They don't seem to help at all now, but if I don't take them I feel awful, so I must need them mustn't I?"

Lou looked concerned. "It *sounds* like it," he answered, "can't you take an extra one, just to keep you going?"

"I could but I don't want to." I knew I would probably feel better if I did increase the dose, but something – either intuition or common sense – kept me from taking that option.

"I'll make you something to eat," I said, and made my way into the kitchen to prepare his lunch. I took longer than usual to cook it, chattering brightly, but all the time hoping inside that he wouldn't go back to work. Not yet anyway.

It wasn't long before he finished his meal and looked at his watch. "I'll have to get back now love," he said, stretching his long legs before he got up from the armchair. The fear began to build up again slowly, in the pit of my stomach. "Try not to worry," he said gently, "it won't be long before the kids are back from school. Just a couple of hours or so. That's not too bad is it?" I shook my head and watched as he picked up his car keys. "See you tonight then, I shouldn't be late."

I watched as he walked to the door, patting me on the head as he went.

"Bye," I smiled at him as he left. On the surface I appeared calm and collected – but inside a voice was screaming, "Please don't go! Please stop here with me!"

Soon that voice was to become more and more insistent – till it would come out at screaming pitch, only stopping when its plea was fulfilled.

*   *   *   *   *

"I hate feeling like this, I really do," I told Dr. Dawson at my next visit, "but I don't want any more anti-depressants. They really don't seem to be doing me any good."

He glanced through my notes. "Yes – you've had quite a few different ones, haven't you. And you say you've never felt any benefits from them at all?"

"No – none that I can think of," I said shaking my head. "They just seem to knock me off balance and make me dizzy.

They also make my eye ache." I had a long-standing eye complaint and some drugs seemed to aggravate this. Dr. Dawson didn't seem surprised.

"That's an understandable reaction. You see water-retention can be one of the side effects of anti-depressants and, as has happened in your case, this stops the fluid draining from the back of the eye; subsequently pressure builds up there and this causes the pain."

I nodded my head in agreement. "I realise that. That's one of the reasons I don't like taking them. Oh. And another thing – if I do take them for a few days and then stop them, I feel really dreadful for a while – sort of all shaky and full of panic."

Dr. Dawson leaned back in his chair and stroked his chin with his hand.

"That's probably because the anti-depressant actually makes the tranquilliser stronger, in the same way that alcohol would, so when you stop taking one it means the strength of the other is reduced."

"I see," I said, "so are these feelings withdrawal symptoms from the tranquilliser?"

"No, I shouldn't think so," he answered, "it's more likely to be your anxiety coming through," he sat forward again and turned back the pages of my file. "Now let me see, you've been on Valium quite a long time now, haven't you?" I nodded. "Well as I have said before, I don't think they are strong enough any more."

"You are not going to put the dose up, are you?" I interrupted. The thought of that horrified me.

"No – don't worry," he smiled reassuringly, "anyway, because you have taken them for so long your body will have become so accustomed to them that you would have to increase the amount considerably before you would feel any reasonable improvement. No – what I would like to do is to give you something else to take at night." He stopped when he saw the alarm in my face. "Don't worry they're not sleeping tablets."

"What are they then?"

"They are another tranquilliser – quite a new one, in fact. They come in two strengths – 1 mg and 2.5 mg – which gives you some indication of how mild they are."

"What are they called?"

"Lorazepam," he answered, "or you will probably know them better as Ativan." Yes I had heard of them.

"They are very similar to Valium, aren't they?"

"Well," he explained, "they are in the same family. But whereas the effects of Valium are long-lasting – these have a much shorter life."

I bit my bottom lip and thought for a few seconds before speaking again. "Do I have to reduce the Valium at all?"

"No." He shook his head. "Keep on with the dose that you are on now and take one Lorazepam at night."

I felt resigned. "I'll try them and see what happens."

"Good," he reached out for his prescription pad, "I'll put you onto 2.5 mg to start off with, but if you find they are too strong, you can halve them if you want." He wrote out the prescription. "I'm sure you'll find them O.K." He put his pen down and handed it to me with a smile ....

"Please let him be right." I prayed as I walked out of the door, the thoughts racing around inside my head. "Please let these be the answer!"

*   *   *   *   *

It was difficult to decide which was worse: life on Valium and Ativan together or life on Valium alone.

The combination of the two blocked out most of the fear and anxiety, but the side-effects of Ativan, even on a much reduced dose, were quite traumatic. Insomnia was no longer a problem, but on waking I experienced a feeling of nausea which persisted until late morning; my head would ache and my limbs would feel like lead. But worst of all, everything felt *flat* – nothing happy, nothing sad – it was as though I was emotionally dead.

"I don't know what to do," I told Lou, "I just want to feel normal again – not like this."

"You seem to be a bit better taking the Ativan at night," he remarked. "You definitely sleep longer and you don't seem to be so bad-tempered and aggressive."

"Maybe so," I answered, "but it's still awful being like this. My mind is all fuzzy, and I can't think and talk straight; also I feel so very tired and heavy all the time."

"Well why don't you take them only when you really need to – maybe just once or twice a week – it might be better than every night. At least, this way you will get a couple of good night's sleep a week and you won't feel so rotten the rest of the time."

His suggestion seemed to be a good idea, and so from then on I took Ativan just once or twice a week and slept soundly. The "Zombie-like" hangover that came the following morning usually disappeared the day after, but the absence of one problem was immediately replaced by a host of others: the days on which I took just Valium alone were now worse than ever.

I became irritable and morose, and my temper would erupt violently – sometimes without any provocation at all. Coping with any problem, no matter how small, was becoming increasingly difficult, and the fear of going out was now an almost insurmountable problem. I would try and find any excuse in order not to leave the security of home; there I felt safe – but only if there was somebody there to keep me company – the thought of being alone brought on a feeling of total panic.

"Please don't leave me on my own!" I pleaded with Lou, tugging at his arm as he walked towards the door. It was eight-thirty in the morning and he was leaving for work.

"Don't go in today, one more day won't matter!"

"I can't keep on taking days off willy-nilly!" he exclaimed. "I've already had five off this month. They are going to say something soon."

I began to cry, with a mixture of despair and guilt. This fear was something I couldn't explain – not even to myself. No matter how much I tried to talk myself into believing there was nothing to be frightened about, the panic that filled my body still persisted.

Lou's attitude softened slightly. He put his arm around my shoulders and spoke to me gently. "Look, if you are as frightened as that, why don't you ring Eileen? I'm sure she will come over and stay with you for a while."

"No – I don't like to. It sounds so silly telling someone that you can't be alone in your own home. It's like being a baby!"

"I'm sure she'll understand if you explain to her..." he began.

"How *can* I explain!" I interrupted, my voice now becoming higher and more insistent. "I can't explain it to myself. So how can I expect Eileen to understand?"

"Even so – I'm sure she won't mind." He sounded slightly impatient now. "Why don't you phone her up and see?"

I knew I shouldn't be keeping him from his work like this, but this feeling of panic made everything else seem unimportant.

"Can't *you* phone her?" I asked him, not wanting to admit my weakness to anybody else. Not yet, anyway.

"O.K.," he agreed, "I'll see what she says, but then I'll *have* to go otherwise I'm going to be late."

Eileen arrived about an hour later.

"I'm sorry for being a nuisance," I felt I had to apologise, "but I don't feel very well."

"Don't worry about it," she said with a smile, "I don't mind, honestly."

What she didn't realise was that as the months passed by I would become more demanding and these visits of hers would have to become more frequent. I cared very much that such a strain would be put on a friendship I valued deeply, but what else could I do? Being alone in the house was now a completely unthinkable option.

My moods were now wholly governed by the amount of tranquillisers I took. The combination of Valium and Ativan together produced a feeling of total numbness – no matter what happened in the day, the only sensation I had was of unreality and detachment. There were no aggressive outbursts or temper tantrums anymore. I felt as though I was wrapped in a blanket of anaesthesia.

It was horrible. And the only option which seemed open to me was to cut down on the Ativan – which I did – only taking one if I was really desperate for sleep. This meant that Valium became the mainstay of my life once more, and each day became a battle, one rolling painfully into the next. On waking in the morning, I would pull myself out of bed, shaky and weak, and stagger down the stairs; any quick movement bringing on a feeling of faintness. Breakfast consisted of cereal piled high with sugar, toast spread thick with marmalade, a cup of strong tea and – last, but not least – one 5 mg Valium. Gradually as the sugar and Valium took it's toll, the faintness would disappear and I would feel passably human once more.

I now noticed how much my physical appearance was beginning to change. I used to take such a pride in the way I looked, but now my hair was lank and lifeless, my eyes dull and glazed. My complexion became a pale parchment colour – no matter how much fresh air I tried to get.

Funnily enough, it never occurred to me at the time how very much my personality had changed. Like so many other symptoms, it had crept up on me gradually, and I would put it down to tiredness or the 'wrong time of the month'. Little by little however, as the weeks and months passed by, there became far more bad days than good and the way I talked and reacted, especially to difficult situations, I began to recognise as being completely out of character. I became difficult and confused and, despite knowing that all my faults and failings weren't part of the 'real me', I felt nevertheless powerless to do anything about them.

It was as though my mind and body belonged to another person – I felt inhabited by a stranger – and no matter how much the 'real me' shouted to be let out, the new outer shell, that stopped this from happening, became tougher every day.

Christmas 1978

It was Christmas morning 1978, and as usual we sat down to open our presents together. This was something we had done since the children were babies, and still do, even to this day.

The living room was festooned with decorations and the tree was lit up with fairy lights. It all looked very festive, and each chair was piled high with brightly wrapped parcels, of different shapes and sizes. It was all very exciting – now everyone was able to find out what each present contained after days of inquisitive poking and guessing! We always took turns to open one at a time – and Louise, being the eldest of the two, had always been first. Everything seemed perfect, no anxiety or fear, just a warm family picture.

It was my turn and I picked up one that I thought looked like a book. "I'd love to own *Wuthering Heights*," I had hinted to Lou weeks before, "it's my favourite book and I haven't read it for years."

"He must have remembered," I thought as I opened the small parcel. I was right it was a book. It was beautifully bound in red leather with gold edging and lettering. "It's lovely," I said, glancing at the title on the spine. It read *The Tenant of Wildfell Hall*.

"What's this?" I demanded. "This isn't *Wuthering Heights!*"

Lou looked apologetic. "I know," he smiled nervously, "I couldn't get that for love or money, so I thought that would be better than nothing. The girl in the shop said that the authors were sisters and their writings were very similar."

Something snapped inside. I became incensed.

"That's rubbish!" I choked. "They write nothing like each other. If two brothers played football you wouldn't say they had to play the same just because they were related, would you?"

"Well yes – I see your point, but ... "

"Well, what made you buy this?" I interrupted holding up the book, "I've always hated it, ever since we did it at school!"

Louise and Paul sat transfixed, not daring to speak, their faces a mixture of shock, disappointment and sadness. The warm, friendly cocoon, that had been so perfect, was now smashed into tiny fragments.

"You are so bloody ungrateful!" he stormed back. "Anybody else would accept it and not say anything – it's the thought that counts, you know."

"When you are involved, there is no thought," I muttered angrily, "anything will do as far as you're concerned."

"That's *not* true," he replied, defending himself. "I *do* try, but that's not good enough for you, is it?"

The hate and anger began to build up like a big bubble inside. "If that's what you call trying," I retorted, "I'd hate to see you when you're *not!*"

He stood up. "I just can't understand you," he said shaking his head in disbelief. "You always have to spoil everything, don't you?"

"If that's what you think, you know what you can do then, don't you?" I felt positively evil. It didn't matter who got hurt as long as my temper was allowed to run it's course. "Just get out and stay out!" I demanded, "I don't even want to look at you."

"If that's what you really want, I'll go then." He glared at me cold and hard.

"Yes, I do!" the other me screamed at him. But underneath all the hate, a small voice was trying to be heard. "Please don't go. I don't mean all those things. I'm sorry. Please don't go." The voice came and went unnoticed.

As he drove the car out of the drive, I watched from the window, tears flowing down my cheeks. Paul and Louise came to me, and I put my arms around them both.

"I'm sorry I've spoilt Christmas for you," I said.

"You haven't mum," Louise said quietly, touching my arm. Paul smiled up at me and leant his head against my shoulder.

"I'm sorry," I hugged them to me, "I'm so very, very sorry."
Lou returned about one hour later.

"I'm sorry about the book, love," he said.

I smiled at him – the outburst now abated, the temper spent. The volcano inside had erupted and my mind and body felt at peace again. I was a normal human being once more.

But the internal battles continued. The 'real me' seeming increasingly lost inside this cold, new person – one who was capable of a cruel and unpredictable temper, and a heartlessness that no one, least of all myself, could either understand or control.

Autumn 1979

Friends and relations had now come round to accepting this new person I had turned into. They referred to the problem as "trouble with her nerves," and I was now classed as being 'highly strung' and not very strong – mentally or physically. They would make allowances for me, trying, in their own kind but ignorant way, to understand the change in my personality.

But the 'real me' inside hated to be treated in this way. "Don't you see, I want to be like all of you!" I would scream inside. "I'm still the same person underneath you know. The one who copes with all sorts of problems no matter how large; the one who tackles most physical jobs no matter how heavy. I used to be strong like you, but now my body is falling to pieces and I don't know why."

The monthly trips to the psychiatrist still continued. Dr. Dawson had given up prescribing different drugs and just gave me the regular prescription for Valium at the end of the fifteen minute consultation. During this time he would discuss the increasing agoraphobia and fear.

"This," he diagnosed, "is probably due to an insecure childhood."

It seemed to be a logical explanation and, because I trusted his judgement entirely, I accepted it without question. "Tranquillisers should help to alleviate these symptoms," he added.

And so I took him at his word, although the trouble was, they didn't seem to be helping me at all; in fact the phobias seemed to be becoming more noticeable to others, and the fear was growing daily. I explained this to him.

"Hmm," he remarked thoughtfully, pursing his lips, "that is very strange. Are you still taking the Ativan at night?"

"Now and then – well, that is about once, or sometimes twice, a week."

"You can take them more often than that you know," he said, "as I have said before they are very mild."

"Yes I know that – it's just that I don't like taking too many pills."

He shrugged his shoulders and gave me a resigned sort of smile. "O.K. then," he said, "it's entirely up to you. It's just that you say you can hardly go out unless there is someone with you and even then it is an effort."

I nodded my head. "I never used to be like this," I told him, "I just don't know why it has happened, I really don't."

"These things happen, sometimes without any obvious reason. I think that in your case, however, it goes back a long way. I also believe that when you learn to accept your past as being over and done with, things will most definitely improve."

As always I believed him. After all, he was a top consultant psychiatrist; full of experience and, as I thought at the time, full of wisdom.

But as the weeks rolled by, my anxiety grew, slowly but surely eating away at my confidence. Any self-respect I *had* had, was now totally fled, and I spent my days shrouded with fear, hating life and, because my mind and body had let me down so much, hating myself.

Because there was no improvement at all in my general health, Lou's normally patient nature began to show signs of strain. The more demands I put onto him, the less tolerant he became, and the smooth running of our life – which had for some time revolved totally around 'my illness' – began to fall apart.

"I can't keep on taking days off work you know. They're going to start saying something soon," his voice was adamant.

"But what can I do? I don't want to be on my own – please don't leave me!" I felt tired and weak and, as usual, full of this unknown fear.

"Well Louise is off school, isn't she? I mean she's not too poorly, so she can be company for you." Louise was suffering from chicken-pox and had been at home for a few days.

"It's not the same!" I clung to his arm, in an attempt to stop him leaving. "Can't you stop with me – please – just for today?"

He wavered for a moment, not knowing what to do. "Well, O.K. But if I stop off today, that will have to be it for a couple of weeks. I can't keep on making excuses."

I relaxed my hold on him and inwardly breathed a sign of relief. I had won once more; he would stop with me today and that was all that mattered. I would worry about tomorrow when it came; it wasn't important at that moment.

Each day was now a constant battle against fatigue, fear and depression: a big black depression that engulfed my whole being, so that I felt myself to be completely worthless, and suicidal thoughts were never far away. My paranoia had grown to the extent that I now believed everything and everyone were against me: I was convinced that friends talked to each other, using every available opportunity to pull me down. Even the 'sane me' inside could see the logic behind this paranoia, "They have every reason to talk about me," I would tell myself, "I mean, let's face it, there's precious little likeable about me now."

*   *   *   *   *

This was the beginning of the blackest period of my life – one in which I felt I was becoming truly insane. My body felt like it no longer belonged to me – it was heavy and numb – and a constant pressure inside my head made me feel as though it was full of water. My vision would blur and I found it difficult to focus. Daylight would hurt my eyes, so sun-glasses were a must every time I ventured outside. Food no longer held any interest for me, meals were something to be endured rather than enjoyed and my digestion had begun to suffer. Even though hospital tests could find nothing wrong, I was convinced I had some dreadful disease eating away at my insides.

There was no reprieve from any of the symptoms as the days rolled into the nights. Sleep was no longer a welcome relief, and I would lie awake in the middle of the night feeling weak, exhausted, afraid and ill; the sleep that finally did come was fitful and full of vivid and restless dreams.

Because of the constant stress that dominated our lives, the relationship between Lou and I suffered greatly: staying on my own was now an unsurmountable problem as there were only so many days when I could rely on friends, so when I needed someone it was mainly Lou I turned to. Some days he seemed to understand, but there were many when he did not; anger and resentment soon began to replace his normal easy-going nature.

"You're not going to start again, are you?" he loomed over me, his face cold and angry.

I couldn't think straight – I felt afraid, but of *what*, I didn't know. I needed someone to hold me close, but at the same time needed to be free. My heart pounded like a drum and my ears were ringing while eveything seemed to be shaking inside. An overwhelming fear had taken over my body and I knew I was going insane. I rocked backwards and forwards, wrapped in despair and panic.

"What the hell is the matter with you?" he stormed. "Why can't you be normal?"

I rocked even harder, wrapping my arms around my body, trying somehow to calm this terror that was within. Tears poured down my face. "I don't know what it is," I cried. "Do you think I'm going mad?"

"You're certainly acting as though you are! Honestly Heather, why can't you pull yourself together?"

I felt an intense dislike for him building up inside. "You think it's so easy, don't you? Well it isn't! I just can't control it – I'm so frightened all the time!"

"I can't understand it!" He glared at me. "I've taken time off work to look after you, what more do you want?"

He had been given a certificate from the doctor allowing him to stay off work for a short while. *Unable to attend work due to wife's nervous debility* it had read. A little while ago this would have been enough to placate me but now it didn't seem to make any difference. The fear ran rampant through my body whether I was alone or not.

I carried on rocking myself, slowly now, finding the movement comforting and secure. "Stop doing that!" he shook my shoulder. "What the hell is the matter with you? You are acting like someone who is out of their mind!"

"Don't!" I sobbed pulling my shoulder away from his grasp. "Just leave me alone – please – just leave me alone!"

"I wish I could," he said coldly, "but if I did walk out you would threaten to do something stupid like you always do. No matter which way I turn you've got me trapped."

"No I haven't!" I cried, jumping to my feet. "Just go if you want. I'm not bothered!" I knew this was a lie and if he did walk out I would completely disintegrate.

"No, I've just told you I can't. I've got no choice – I have to put up with this hell of living here with you."

Now, as had happened so often before, the anger overtook the fear.

"You're the one who's making life hell!" I screamed at him, "I'm ill and you just can't see it. You're so hard – you haven't got a heart."

"*I* haven't got a heart?" he bellowed. "You'd have to be a bloody saint to live in this house with you!"

I tried to defend myself. "I can't help it. I'm *so* afraid!"

"Afraid, afraid – I'm sick of hearing the bloody word! I keep on telling you, there is nothing to be afraid of. Can't you understand that?"

It was the way he said *can't you understand* as though I was stupid. That cut through me as I thought of how quick and alert my mind *used* to be. Why was it letting me down? What was I doing wrong? I went over to the window and watched as two women walked by. They seemed to be in their thirties and chattered brightly as they went along.

"I want to be like them," I thought, "to be able to think, walk and talk like a normal person once more." The window-sill was low enough to sit on. I sank down, dejected.

"Please get me some help," my voice was quiet now, barely audible, "*please*. I think I'm going mad."

"There isn't anyone," he replied, "it's Saturday and the doctors are closed." His voice was hard and unyielding.

"I don't care – ring the hospital or something, there must be somebody there who can help."

He hesitated, looking down at me, bewildered and unsure.

"Please don't let me be like this any more," I continued, "I'll do anything they say."

"Well – all right," he sighed as he spoke, his voice now much softer, "I'll see what I can do."

As he telephoned the hospital I tried to piece things together in my mind. *Something* would have to be done – we couldn't go on any longer like this. I knew he couldn't take much more – his patience had begun to wear thin and his temper was frayed. I moved from the window-sill and sat down on the edge of the settee waiting for him to finish the call.

"They weren't much help," he said as he entered the room. "The doctor who's on call wasn't there, so they suggested you take an extra Valium or Ativan and see if that helps."

I was furious. "I'm not going to do that; I've taken too many already!"

"I can't make you out," he sounded exasperated. "You said that you would do anything they said and now when they suggest something you turn it down. If you don't take what's prescribed for you how do you expect to get well?"

"It wasn't a doctor that told me to take them, though, was it?" I asked.

"No – it was the sister, but surely she must know what she's talking about. She's probably seen loads of people like you."

I was shaking all over, my head felt like it was going to explode.

"I don't care," I shouted angrily, "I just want someone to talk to...someone who will understand!" And I began to feel a panic building up inside. This was too much to take!

"If you don't get me any help, I'll do something crazy, I know I will!" I felt desperate and had begun to think like someone possessed – I could hurt myself, hurt him and the children, smash the house up, do anything just to get help. I was going crazy – couldn't he see that?

"Right! You want help? Well, if that's what you want – you'll get it!" He came across the room in two strides and pulled me to my feet. "Come on, get your coat on, we'll soon have you put away." He looked at my horrified expression. "That's what you want, isn't it?" He gripped my arms tightly, staring coldly into my face.

"You know it's not," my voice came out in jerks. "I've just told you, I need someone to talk to. Someone to tell me I'm not going mad."

"Don't worry, they'll talk to you all right," he pulled me across the room towards the door, "because I am bloody sick of this. Every day is the same... *No* – it's not...it's getting worse! And it is about time they did something about it!"

He went to the hall cupboard and pulled out my coat. "Here put this on!" He threw it at me.

I didn't move. My legs felt as though they were made of stone.

"Come on! What are you waiting for?" He opened the door, bowing his arm as though to show me the way.

Two figures emerged on the stairs. Louise and Paul had tactfully kept out of sight during all of this, but now they obviously felt they had a right to know what was happening.

"It's O.K." Lou told them a little too harshly, "I'm taking your mother to hospital to see if someone can help her. Louise look after Paul, will you?" She nodded and looked at me, her eyes huge and questioning.

Lou stormed downstairs and out to get the car. I knew he was serious: he was going to take me to hospital. I looked at the children and tried to find words to explain. "Don't worry," I told them, "I'll be back soon, you'll see. Just don't go out until we come back, will you?" But they just stared back bewildered – searching for answers in my face: I knew that no matter what I said they were missing out on a normal childhood and were growing up thinking their mother was a mad-woman.

Lou drove to the hospital in cold silence. I didn't want to speak either. What was the point? This force that had taken over my mind and body had won. I felt beaten, defeated.

The Psychological Medicine In-Patients Unit was a tall flat-fronted building with many tiny windows set in rows. Once inside I noticed how quiet it seemed compared to other hospital departments. A young nurse came up to us wth a smile.

"Are you looking for someone?" she asked.

"Yes," replied Lou, "can you tell me where I can find the sister, please?"

"Turn right at the top of the stairs and it's the second door on the left."

I followed Lou up the stairs, no longer feeling any fear, just overwhelmed by a total sense of defeat. So this was where I belonged: in a psychiatric hospital. Somehow I had to come to terms with that horrific and desperate fact.

The sister was a jolly little plump woman. "Can I help at all?" Her face crinkled as she smiled at us. I made no effort to answer her back.

"Let him speak!" I thought petulantly, "he brought me here, so let him explain!"

"Yes, this is my wife, Heather Jones." It was as though he had read my thoughts. "I rang you earlier about her."

"Ah yes – I remember. You said she was having a few problems and needed to see a doctor."

They both looked at me for a few moments as though waiting for me to say something. I hung my head, staring at the floor.

"Well as I said on the telephone, Mr. Jones, the doctor on call isn't here at the moment, but he shouldn't be too long," she glanced at her fob-watch. "In fact, he's probably on his way right now."

"Will it be Dr. Dawson?" I said, finding my tongue at last.

"No. He won't be here until Monday morning. It's the registrar who's on duty this morning."

I felt uneasy and awkward. How would this doctor know what was wrong; he didn't know anything about me? Maybe I should wait? I mean, what was the point of wasting their time and mine?

"Do you think it would be best if I came back on Monday, then?"

"Well you're here now," she coaxed gently, "so why don't you let him have a word with you? He's just a young doctor, but he's very good. I'm sure he'll be able to help."

I looked at Lou for advice. His face was concerned and he spoke gently now. "Come on, love," he said, "you might as well, we're here now."

I nodded slowly, "What does it matter?" I thought. I didn't believe that anyone could help me – so it didn't matter who it was that I saw.

The sister picked up the telephone on her desk and dialled one number. "Hello - it's Sister Elliot here. Is Doctor Meredith around? He is? Good, that's great. Thankyou." She put the receiver back on the rest. "He's on his way here," she said, "so you won't have to wait very long. If you just hang on a minute, I'll get a nurse to take you somewhere you can sit."

"Thanks very much," Lou smiled at her as she left the room, but I felt a sudden surge of panic and anxiety. "Don't worry, love," he said noticing the expression on my face, his attitude now kind and soft. "It'll be all right, just wait and see."

"But I don't really want to be here," I told him quietly. "I don't think the doctor will be able to help me, do you?"

He smiled and reached out and touched my hand. "You never know, he might be able to suggest something. Let's wait and see."

I nodded, resigned, but I knew in my heart he'd have to be a miracle- worker to put me right.

"Would you like to come this way?" A small nurse dressed in pale blue suddenly appeared in the doorway. She chattered brightly as we followed her along the corridor. As we passed one of the rooms I glanced in. There were several people inside all standing around a tea-trolley. Nothing unusual about that, you would say, apart from the fact that the elderly gentleman, who was pouring tea from a huge pot, wore a black riding-hat. "Oh dear God," I thought, "what am I doing here?"

The nurse had stopped outside a door at the end of the corridor. "You should be all right in here," she said as she stepped inside, "this is the quiet room." It wasn't very large – in fact it was almost cosy and several easy chairs were placed around the walls.

"Will I have to wait long?" I asked her. I could feel the tears building up, stinging the back of my eyes. I hated this place and just wanted to run away.

"No, the doctor should be here very shortly. Don't worry they'll soon put you right."

The nurse's voice was sincere enough, but I suddenly had this uncontrollable urge to laugh out loud. Instead, without thinking, I began to recite in my head,

"Humpty Dumpty sat on a wall, Humpty Dumpty had a great fall, All the king's horses and all the king's men Couldn't put Humpty together again."

Oh – if only she knew it was going to take more than one young doctor to "put me right". Even if there was a whole hospital full of them, they couldn't put *me* together again.

The next ten minutes seemed like a lifetime. Lou had buried his head in a magazine. Every now and then he would look up and raise his eyebrows in acknowledgement, but he didn't speak a word.

"I wonder what he'll be like, this young doctor?" I thought. "He's probably some upstart who thinks he knows everything. Oh, why can't it be Dr. Dawson. At least he knows my medical background. I don't want to start having to explain everything to some stranger who probably hasn't got a clue."

"Heather Jones?" A slim-faced, dark-haired young man poked his head around the door. I nodded in acknowledgement. "Hi – I'm Simon Meredith." He grinned at Lou and I. "Sister says you want to have a few words with someone; maybe I can help?"

As he entered the room Lou put his magazine down and stood up. I noticed Dr. Meredith was tall – a bit shorter than Lou – but still tall, and I nodded back, but felt no urge to return his cheerful smile. He looked at me for a second or two. "Would you like to come with me?" he asked, "there's a room further along that's a bit more private, you never know who's going to come in here."

"O.K." I glanced at Lou and stood up.

"Should I just stay here?" Lou asked.

The doctor turned to him. "Yes, just for a short while, if you don't mind. I'd like to have a word with your wife first on her own and then, if you like, I'll have a word with both of you together. O.K?"

"Yes. That's fine." Lou sat back down and picked up his magazine again.

Without looking at him I followed Dr Meredith out of the room and back along the corridor. "It's just down here," he glanced over his shoulder at me as he walked along, "not very far."

He took long and easy strides and I had to walk quickly in order to keep up; eventually he stopped outside a door marked Duty Doctor. "Here we are," he said opening the door, "it's not fantastic but at least it's private."

The room was even smaller than the last one, and facing us was a black swivel-chair which was situated behind a large desk. I thought he was going to sit in this chair, but he went over to one of two smaller armchairs that were against the wall, picked it up and placed it in the middle of the room so it was facing the other. He sat down on this, at the same time beckoning me to sit down opposite. "All right?" he stretched his long legs across the space between us and folded his arms across his chest. He was still smiling.

"Oh my God," I thought, "I can't stand this. Why is he so bloody cheerful?" and I stared back coldly. He wasn't as young as I thought he would be – late twenties, maybe even early thirties – but his athletically slim build belied his age. He wore brown flannels with soft shoes, and his fawn sports-jacket had leather patches on the elbows; a deer-stalker hat sat on the desk.

"I hear you are having a few problems, well how about telling me about them?" He spoke very quietly in a reassuring tone, but in spite of his manner I felt the urge to snap.

"*I* don't know what the problems are," I said sharply, "I thought you would tell me!" But in spite of my outburst and the glaring look I gave him, he seemed unperturbed and spoke gently to me again.

"Well I'll try, but you'll have to tell me a bit about yourself first."

"I really don't see any point in doing that," I replied defiantly, "Dr. Dawson knows everything there is to know and in any case, I wouldn't know where to start."

"How about at the beginning."

I gave a sarcastic laugh. "The beginning? What beginning? The day I was born, or the start of this – this, what would I call it – mess?"

"Is that what you think it is – a mess?"

"Of course it is unless you can think of another word for it."

His gaze never faltered, unnerving me slightly. "I won't know until you tell me all the things that you think are causing this 'mess'."

My retort was still sarcastic. "Huh! Do you want the list in writing? There are so many, that even if I did tell you, you wouldn't be able to remember them all!"

"Oh I'm sure I would." He seemed very sure of himself.

"Well I don't want to go into that at the moment, O.K?" I was trying to annoy him, but he remained unruffled.

"Anything you want," he said, "we'll talk about something else if you like."

God, he was annoying me. Why was he so self-assured? Why wasn't he losing his cool? I glared at him, hostile and aloof. He wasn't going to get through to me, no matter how much he tried. It was Dr. Dawson I needed; safe Dr. Dawson with his bag of pills.

I began to feel uncomfortable and restless. "What is he thinking?" I asked myself. "He's probably realising what a pain I am. I bet he's dying to leave but knows he can't."

It was then that I began to look at this young doctor with defiant interest. He had quite a kind and pleasant face, and his hair, thick and wavy, was rich dark brown in colour. But it was his eyes that held my attention: they, too, were brown – but they seemed so quiet – large and deep, as though they would never reveal what he was really thinking.

He smiled again, biting his bottom lip as he did so, and the vulnerable appearance this gave him caused my resentment towards him to soften.

"I don't really think I should be here," I said quietly, "I'm sorry if I'm wasting your time." He nodded his head, but didn't speak. "It's just that earlier this morning I felt so ill," I carried on, "and I don't know why."

"What do you mean by 'ill'?"

"Well I couldn't stop shaking, not outwardly but inside, and I feel so very tired, but not sleepy, as though I've got 'flu' all the time. Oh – and worst of all – I've got this dreadful fear."

"What fear is this?" He sat up slightly in his chair, crossing his legs one over the other.

"An awful fear – I can't explain it. It seems worse if I'm left on my own or if I have to go out. Not necessarily *outside* in the garden, you understand, but if I have to go to the shops or anywhere where there will be a lot of people."

"What do you think will happen to you if you do go to these places?"

"I don't know. Probably pass out or something, I suppose."

Have you ever passed out?" he asked.

I thought for a moment. "Yes, once or twice. Once when I was pregnant with Lousie."

"Louise?"

"Yes, she is my eldest child."

"How many children do you have?"

"I've got one more – Paul – he's ten and Louise is nearly fourteen."

"That's nice." He rested his chin on his hand. "Anyway, you were talking about this fear. How long have you had it now?"

"Oh, one year – maybe getting on for two, now. I can't really put a date on it – sort of crept up on me without me realising it."

"I believe you take a tranquilliser?"

"Yes, that's right – Valium, 5mg three times a day. Oh – and I sometimes take Ativan at night."

He lifted his head off his arm and sat upright. "Did Dr. Dawson prescribe these for you or did you G.P?"

"Dr. Dawson prescribed Ativan, but I originally got Valium from my G.P. about eight years ago."

He seemed alert now and almost clinical.

"Eight years?" he remarked. "That's a very long time. What are you taking them for?"

"Anxiety, I think. I don't really know."

"And you've had anxiety for eight years?" He sounded amazed.

"Well...no. I was first given them to cope with Paul when he was a baby. He was hyperactive and wouldn't sleep. Then later on I had a miscarriage and the doctor prescribed a higher dose." He watched me all the time I was speaking; the huge, quiet eyes unblinking. "I don't think they're doing any good though," I continued, "I mean I've got more anxiety now than I've ever had in my life. I never had this much before I started taking them; things seem to be getting worse instead of better, and I'm so depressed all the time."

"Is that what Dr. Dawson is treating you for – depression?"

"Yes – but the pills he gives me make the symptoms worse, especially when I stop taking them."

He nodded and pursed his lips. "I see...well without seeing your records I can't be sure exactly, but I must admit – I don't think that pills are the answer."

I looked at him quickly; a slight hope flickered inside. "Do you really think so?" I asked. "You see I hate taking them, but I thought I needed to for my anxiety and depression."

"Well personally I don't like prescribing drugs – not on a long-term basis, anyway – in my opinion anxieties and fears, especially in your case, come from within. Pills only cover up the problems. They don't make them go away."

I wanted to hear more. "What do you suggest then? Because I can't stand living like this much longer."

"Well I would recommend Psychotherapy," he answered.

"What's that?" I said.

"It means treating the problem through the mind, rather than with drugs, and it involves extensive analysis. It can be a rather long and drawn-out process so you sometimes have to wait for a therapist to be free."

"Oh I see, it's not a psychiatrist that does it then?"

"Well, yes, it usually is," he replied, "but because the treatment is so lengthy, the psychiatrist usually has only one therapy patient at a time."

"Does that mean I wouldn't see Dr. Dawson any more?" I felt a slight panic inside.

"If you were accepted as a patient in need of Psychotherapy then, yes, I'm afraid that that would be so."

"How do I know if I'm suitable or not?"

"Well you would be given a questionnaire to fill in – nothing difficult, just mainly asking about your case history – then you would be given an interview with a consultant psychotherapist who would assess your case. If he thinks that you would benefit, he will arrange for you to see someone as soon as possible."

"How long would the treatment go on for?" I inquired.

"Usually about a year, sometimes a bit longer."

"As long as that?" I raised my eyebrows in surprise.

"Yes, I'm afraid so. As I've just said it is very extensive. You see, your brain is like a filing cabinet and sometimes it can get very untidy. When this happens you can get very confused and can't think straight. During therapy we take out all your fears, anxieties and any other negative feelings – examine them and come to terms with them, and then file them back in the right order." This seemed to make sense.

"But what about the tranquillisers? Will I have to come off them?" I needed reassurance.

"Well, we'd definitely think about reducing them. I think it is about time you did this anyway – eight years is really far too long." He sat up on the edge of his chair. "Should I go and get your husband so we can discuss it? He probably thinks we've forgotten about him by now."

I smiled at him for the first time and nodded my head. He disappeared out of the door and I felt happier than I had done in months. "I just *know* this is the answer," I thought excitedly, "I *knew* the drugs weren't doing me any good!"

*   *   *   *   *

"I feel like I'm getting a cold," I told Joan; we were glancing through a mail-order catalogue together. It was Friday evening and, although for the past five years this had been regarded as 'the girls'night out', these were now becoming a rarity and I would make any conceivable excuse in order to stay at home.

In the beginning Joan didn't seem to mind, but as the excuses became more and more feeble, she became more suspicious. "You know if you don't like going out together any more, just say so," she would say.

"No – it isn't that," I would try and explain, "it's just that I don't like going anywhere these days."

"Well, we can go somewhere quiet, if you want," she suggested, "and if you feel funny we can come home early."

"Can we leave it until next week?" I would ask. "I might feel different then." But I knew, even as I spoke, that I would feel exactly the same.

"Well, as long as it isn't something I've said or done." She had sounded irritable and I could understand why; I was letting everyone down these days. I wished I could make them understand – but it seemed impossible to explain my unreasonable behaviour to others when I couldn't explain it to myself.

An icy-cold shiver ran through my body as Joan turned the page of the catalogue. "I really don't feel right," I told her, as my head throbbed, my eyes stung and I ached all over. I hadn't felt well for a few days now but had put it down to the general state of my health.

"Maybe it's the 'flu'," she replied, and I was beginning to think she might be right. But later that evening, two blisters emerged on my arm and the following morning there were several more. I had chicken-pox.

The next two days were spent in total oblivion. My temperature soared to 106 and the higher it went, the more the spots appeared. My long-standing eye complaint became aggravated by the virus and flared up so I could only see out of one eye. The doctor, who had been out every day, prescribed two different antibiotics. "You must take them," she insisted. "We don't want you catching pneumonia on top of everything else."

By the fourth day I began to feel slighty better so I thought I would try and get up for a while. I couldn't have made a bigger mistake! I began to shake from head to foot as perspiration poured down my back and an awful panic ran through my body, leaving me drained and breathless.

"Oh dear God," I said to Lou, clinging onto him, "it must be worse than I thought." And as he helped me back to bed I asked him to bring me a Valium. I had only taken the odd one over the past few days and my head felt as though it was going to explode.

Lou's face showed his concern. "Perhaps it's just the effects of the chicken-pox: you have been quite ill, you know."

I hoped – and prayed – that he would be right. "Yes," I
thought to myself, "when my strength builds up I'll feel a lot
better. I'll soon pick up."

But that hoped-for recovery somehow never arrived. I didn't
know it at the time, but stopping the tablets during that bout of
chicken-pox had given me a taste of withdrawal. Neither did I
realize that I still had a long way to go on the downward path,
before I was to understand that withdrawal from tranquillisers
was to be my only way up.

1979 – 1980

"Would you like to wait in here?" the nurse showed me into a large sitting-room, where several women – either reading or knitting – sat in small groups.

'Here' was Clayton Hall, a large Victorian house, situated on the outskirts of the city centre amidst the University buildings. It had originally been the home of a wealthy business man, but had recently been converted into a half-way house for people with psychological problems. I sat down at the far end of the room. So this is where I would be coming for the next year or so...

It was now a month since I had first been seen by the Consultant Psychotherapist. His letter had arrived one week later. *I am pleased to inform you* it had read, *that you have been accepted for a course of Psychotherapy. I have spoken with Dr Simon Meredith, who has agreed to see you on a weekly basis. He will arrange for an appointment and contact you as soon as possible. Yours sincerely, Dr. Hugh Leeming, Consultant Psychotherapist*

I had received Dr Meredith's appointment ten days ago. "I am really pleased it is him," I had told Lou. "At least I will have an idea of what to expect."

"Where do you have to see him?" he had asked. "The Western General Hospital?"

"No, it's somewhere called Clayton Hall. It's near the University." I had pointed to the letter. "Anyway there's a map on the back of this telling us how to get there."

"Well I hope this treatment is going to work." He had sounded unsure.

"I'm *sure* it will," I had quickly replied. Surely, *something* had to work for me, *soon*.

Now, as I waited, this hope was uppermost in my mind. It wasn't long before Dr. Meredith's voice could be heard in the hall; he seemed to be chatting to a patient. "How are you now? Good – that's great. I'll try and see you later, O.K?" A few seconds later he glanced into the room.

"Hi Heather – I see you found us all right?" He sounded as bright and cheerful as usual. I nodded and smiled at him. "Would you like to come with me?" he asked.

I followed him out of the room and across the hall, his soft shoes squeaking on the floor as he strode along, until we got to a door marked 'Private', which led onto a small corridor with a room on either side.

"Here we are," he announced as he opened one of the doors. "It's not the Ritz, but at least it's nice and quiet." He pulled up two chairs so they faced each other. "Please take a seat. Alright?" he asked as we sat down.

"Yes, fine," I nodded, noticing once more how much of the floor space between us was taken up by his long legs. He lounged back in his chair, feet crossed, hands folded across his stomach. He looked completely at ease and I sat on the edge of my seat, upright and sightly tense.

"Well," he began, "I hear you haven't been too well. Chicken-pox, wasn't it?"

"Yes that's right – and I still have the marks to prove it!" I smiled as I pointed to my arms and face where there were still faint reminders of the virus. He looked me up and down. "Don't worry I'm not infectious any more," I added, noticing his gaze.

He laughed softly. "Yes I *do* know that."

"Oh, I'm sorry – of course you do!" I lowered my head and bit my bottom lip in mock apology, smiling up at him; it was so easy to forget he was a doctor.

He uncrossed his hands and sat up slightly, "Tell me though, apart from the chicken-pox, how have you been?"

"Oh – not too bad," I replied, "I haven't been out that much though, mainly because of the marks on my face."

He looked at me. "They're not very noticeable and they will go away in time."

"Yes, I know. It's just that I haven't got much confidence now anyway – and looking like this has made me even worse."

"You look O.K. to me."

I smiled. "Thanks for saying so, but...it's just...oh, I don't know. Maybe I'm looking for excuses again."

He put his hand to his mouth and began to gnaw gently at one of his knuckles – a habit, I was to notice, he would adopt whenever he was concentrating. "You told me at our first meeting that you've been like this for quite a long time now. Can you remember if anything happened to you that might have triggered these feelings off?"

I shook my head. "Nothing that I can think of specifically," I said. "You see, it was such a gradual process that I can't remember exactly when it began. And this is what worries me – I *never* used to be like this. In fact I always had loads of confidence and I was not in the least bit frightened of being on my own."

"I see...but now you are?"

"Yes. And I wish I wasn't. I'm sure that people must think I'm mad..."

"Does it matter to you what people think?"

"Yes, I suppose it does. More than it ever did before. In fact I hate it if I think someone doesn't like me."

He nodded as I spoke. "So you reckon you've always been insecure when it comes to other peoples' feelings towards you?"

"Yes, I suppose I have," I answered slowly, "but it never mattered to me as much as now. Before it wasn't a problem, but now it is."

He moved slightly to one side of his seat, leaning his head on his hand. "The other thing you mentioned last time was that you were feeling generally unwell – physically that is."

"Yes, I still do," I replied. "Some days I feel completely weak and washed out. My muscles ache, I have this awful pressure in my head and I don't seem to have any coordination at all – it's a bit like 'flu', but without the temperature."

"And are these symptoms getting any worse?" he asked.

"No – not really, some days they won't be too bad, but then they come back without any warning." I leaned back in my chair now, relaxing slightly. Simon didn't speak and his gaze, steady and unfaltering, prompted me to continue. "When these feelings are especially bad, my mind becomes all confused, and I can't think or speak properly – it's as though I'm not really here. This is when I begin to think I'm going mad." I looked at him urgently, "but I'm not going mad am I?"

He shook his head with a smile and spoke reassuringly. "Let me put your mind at rest straight away, you are not, as you put it 'going mad'. People who *are* – for the want of a better word – mad, have no realisation of the fact; they think they're normal. No – the symptoms you have described can sometimes occur when the anxiety level is high, or the person is in a depressed state..."

"I know," I interrupted, "that's what Dr Dawson used to say. But I don't *have* any reason to be depressed or anxious – so why is it that some days I feel as though my whole body is falling to pieces?"

"Are you eating and sleeping alright?" he asked.

"No – neither, I get off to sleep all right, but then I wake up three or four hours later. I'm getting awful stomach pains as well, so whether these wake me up or not I don't know."

"Have you had these pains seen to?"

"Yes, I've had two X-rays and an endoscopy. But they didn't spot anything."

"You only get these pains at night?"

"No, I get them during the day as well, but they're worse at night."

He was silent for a few moments as though deep in thought, and then raised his head from his arm. "And what about your appetite?"

"That's not very good either, I wish it were!" I had always been on the slim side, but now the weight loss was beginning to be noticeable. "But what's causing all these feelings? There must be something wrong, mustn't there?"

He sat forward in his chair. "Most of these symptoms are, or at least can be, the result of chronic anxiety..." He paused when I opened my mouth to protest, but quickly continued. "Now I know that you say there is no obvious reason why you should be anxious, but I think that deep down there is – and that's why we're here. We want to find out *what* the reason is and then, by helping you to face up to it, to stop it from making you so anxious. Does that make sense?"

"So you think my anxiety is caused by something hidden in my murky past?" I smiled, mocking him slightly.

He grinned back, with a boyish expression. "So you've got a murky past?"

"Well, I wouldn't say *murky* exactly, just shady in parts!"

"I see," he nodded, smiling, "well it's the shady parts that we want to find out about."

I looked at him, quite seriously now. "And you definitely think that it's because of things that happened years ago that I'm feeling so ill now?"

"I believe the anxiety is *contributing* towards your ill-health, and that this is caused by something deep-rooted you can't yet put your finger on."

"Do you mean something that happened when I was very young?"

"Possibly so – we won't know until we discuss it in depth."

"And how far will we have to go back?"

"As far as you want."

"And what happens if I can't remember?"

"That's unlikely: more often than not, you will. That's what psychotherapy is for."

I thought for a few minutes before speaking.

"I can remember as far back as when I was three."

"That's fine. In fact the most important years are the formative ones, from when you were six or seven up until your late teens."

"Oh yes," I reflected, "I can remember those well."

"So that's mainly what we'll discuss each week," he explained, "examining them in detail, bit by bit. Then hopefully, by doing this, we'll find out the reasons for your anxieties and fears."

It seemed to make sense and I was happy with this arrangement. "It doesn't matter how many years it takes," I thought, " at least I'm going to be free of all this in the end!"

*　*　*　*　*

My whole world now revolved around the weekly visits to Simon Meredith. I believed in him totally, and couldn't visualise life without him being part of it; he was my lifeline.

As the weeks progressed the more intense the analysis became. Simon was relentless: poking and prodding at my innermost feelings and fears till he'd bullied and coaxed them out into the open, pulling them up by their stubborn roots.

I relived my childhood, examining every possible event which could have led to my present state: my parents' divorce; the long years of separation from my mother – unprepared and unexplained – and life with my dear father, a man who had a gentle, almost feminine softness, but who at the same time possessed great strength, especially in times of need. I lived happily with him until his untimely death in 1962. I was then seventeen years old.

"I can see why you don't like being on your own," Simon explained. "It's probably due to losing your mother, your father, and finally your home."

"But why didn't feel like this years ago?" I asked.

"That we can't explain, but sometimes these fears lie dormant for years, buried in the subconscious, until something comes along to trigger them off."

"But why can't I cope with stress at all? That can't be because of this, can it?"

"Constant anxiety can produce this reaction, and while you still have all your fears and phobias you'll still find stress difficult to cope with."

"So it's a vicious circle is it?" I remarked.

"Yes, until you can come to terms with the problems in your past life and accept them."

"And talking about them helps you do that, does it?"

"Yes, that's right, talking them through – over and over, if necessary."

"Well, that's what we're doing isn't it?" I must have been beginning to sound restless.

"Yes, we are, but there is a long way to go yet."

"But it seems never-ending." Six months had now passed since I had started psychotherapy and patience was not my virtue!

"We can't hurry," he said shaking his head, "it has to be done slowly to make sure that we don't miss anything."

"I *know* that," I replied. "It's just that I don't seem to be getting anywhere. In fact things are worse, if anything."

"How are you getting on with the Valium?" he asked.

"Not *too* bad," I sounded unsure. "You did say that the withdrawal was nothing to worry about?" I had cut down from 15 mg to 10 mg over a period of three months.

"Yes, that's right," he answered. "You may suffer a little increased anxiety, but it shouldn't be anything too severe."

"Yes," I agreed, "I've noticed that – and I'm getting very jumpy too. And another thing is that my bowel keeps going into spasms – a bit like a mild labour pain – especially for the first couple of days or so, and then they and the other symptoms level out again."

"That's good," he said with a smile. "Don't worry we'll soon have you off them."

*   *   *   *   *

And so the visits continued, week by week, month by month. Many times I would return home in tears, nursing open wounds.

"I'm not going back any more," I would cry to Lou. "I'm getting worse, not better!"

"You don't have to go if you don't want to, you know," Lou would reply.

But I did go back, determined to see it through; determined, if I possibly could, to get better. It wasn't always tears. I relived the laughter too: the childhood hopes and dreams – some of which had been realised, and some of which hadn't. These happy sessions made the others worthwhile.

But I never got any better. In fact the anxiety and fears became greater and the depressions became blacker. Being on my own was now my biggest problem. "It's because I was on my own when my father died," I told Lou.

"But I thought you were learning to accept all that." He seemed annoyed.

"Well, maybe I have to get worse before I get better," I replied defensively.

"I hope so, because I don't want to be off work indefinitely," he said. He had given up his job up several weeks ago. His firm had been very understanding about the problem, but the constant 'days off' had made the outcome inevitable.

The letter asking for his resignation had been pleasant but final.

Dear Mr Jones, it had read. *Because of your increasing absence from work, it is with much regret that we will have to ask you to temporarily terminate your employment with us. We realise that this is due to your wife's illness, so if, at a later date, her health improves and you feel you could continue working once more, we will be only too pleased to consider you for employment again. In the meantime we would like to take this opportunity to thank you for the excellent service you have given the Company and to wish you well for the future.*

I knew this was bound to happen sooner or later, but when it happened I felt an overwhelming sense of guilt and despair. I beat my fists and sobbed at the unfairness of it all.

The more I had turned to doctors for help, the blacker the future had become. I had followed their instructions, obeyed their rules, but the long-sought-for relief had eluded me. Now Lou had lost his job, and our world was crumbling about us.

And still nobody knew the reason why.

1980 – 1983

My hands shook as I fumbled with the fastener on my skirt. "I must try harder tonight," I told myself, "if only for Paul's sake." I clung onto the dressing table, my knuckles white, the perspiration clinging to my clothes.

Tonight, a concert was being held at the school and Paul had one of the leading roles. "I have to go," my heart pounded in my chest, "I can't let him down. If only this fear would go away, I'd be alright."

The fear had come to dominate my life and now over-rode all other reasoning. I had been seeing Simon for nearly two years now, long over the expected length of treatment. "I can't stop seeing him yet," I would tell Lou. "I don't know what I will do if he decides to finish the therapy, I really don't." I needed him. He was my crutch, my safety-net, always there to cushion any knocks or blows.

As Simon had changed hospitals over the years – so had the venues of our meetings. He had guided me along the complicated path of my life, digging out the rubbish, smoothing over the rough edges, so that I now acknowledged and understood all the past traumas; all the old resentments and bitternesses had long gone.

But the fear still raged with an even greater intensity than before. To add to this there were now new symptoms – ones that had gradually crept in over the years. I now suffered from a continual pain in my side together with bowel cramps and frequent attacks of diarrhoea. Hospital tests had failed to find anything specifically wrong with me and "Irritable Bowel

Syndrome" had been eventually diagnosed. This meant that my need to go to the loo was both frequent, unpredictable and urgent – adding to my other fears about going out. "I'm frightened in case I have to go to the toilet," I would say. My diet had become very sparse – I could eat only very bland foods – and I had become anaemic. Despite regular dental treatment, I had also developed recurring mouth abscesses. I was a physical wreck.

"Well, we're here," said Lou as we pulled into the school car-park. I swallowed hard and tried to take a deep breath, my hands clenched together in my lap.

"I wish it was all over." I said anxiously.

"Don't worry. You'll be alright." Lou reassured me. I gave him a doubtful smile.

We made our way to the main entrance and into the school foyer. Two girls, obviously pupils, were in attendance at the door. "Would you like to go straight into the dining hall and take a seat," one of them said, "the meal will be served shortly?"

"Meal? Seat?" I clutched Lou's arm. "It said 'buffet' on the ticket!" I had presumed that this would have been held after the concert, not before, which would have meant I could have tucked myself away in a corner somewhere or, if necessary, slipped away unnoticed.

As we walked into the hall my worst fears were realised. The tables, about thirty altogether, were each laid out for six people. Lou sat down at one near to the door and beckoned me to sit next to him. "Oh, dear God!" I thought, the panic building up inside like a massive bubble, "please let me be alright!"

Gradually the room began to fill up until nearly all the seats were occupied. I tried to speak to the two other couples who shared our table but my face froze into a plastic smile. Drums began to pound in my ears; circles of blackness appeared before my eyes blurring their vision; my tongue swelled to twice it's size, making it impossible to swallow, and the walls of the dining hall seemed to be contracting and dilating before my eyes. I was slipping down a black tunnel.

"I'm going to faint," I thought, "please let me get out!" And with an effort that sapped every ounce of my strength, I pulled myself back to reality and slowly stood up. "I won't be a minute," I gasped to Lou and before he could answer I fled from the room.

I hurried all the way home, my legs buckling underneath me as though they were made of jelly, my face and body burning despite the cold night air.

I fell into the warmth and welcome of the house; it's safety felt like an embrace. The lounge was empty – Louise must have been upstairs with the throat infection that had kept her from the concert – and I slumped into an easy chair, engulfed with despair and shame. As the final traces of the panic ebbed away, Louise appeared in the doorway.

"What's the matter, mum," she asked, "why have you come home so soon?"

I looked at her. She was growing up fast; turned sixteen and now a young woman. If I told her would she be old enough to understand? I tried to find the words.

"I just felt really ill," I explained slowly, "sort of faint and dizzy. I didn't know that we were going to have to sit down to eat. If it had just been a buffet meal I would have probably been alright."

"Did you see Paul at all?" she asked.

Disappointment and guilt immediately welled up in my heart and hot tears stung the backs of my eyes. I had let him down – let them all down – I was useless, a failure, with no point to my life at all.

"What's the matter with me, Louise?" I asked. "Why do these feelings keep on taking me over?"

"I don't know, mum," she sat down on the floor near my feet. "Did dad come back with you?"

"No. He's still at the school I think." At one time he would have followed me home but these days he was becoming more detached, more aloof from me and my illness; his once placid nature now frequently giving way to out-bursts of physical and verbal abuse.

"Ah well, don't worry then," Louise said, touching my arm. "He won't be long. Why don't you have a nice cup of tea? I'll make you one if you want."

"That would be nice. Can I have my evening Valium, too?"

"Alright," she smiled as she stood up. "You'll soon feel better, just wait and see."

I nodded my head, eyes downcast. Why couldn't I function like a normal person? I was a failure – a complete failure. The bottom was dropping out of my world.

Lou was quiet when he returned home. "You missed a good show," he declared. "Paul and his friend were great." I felt so ashamed, so weak. But the following day those frustrated feelings were turning into anger.

"I'm so sick of this!" I cried. "Every day is the same. I just don't want to go on like this anymore!"

"Well, do something about it then." His voice was cold and grim.

"Such as what?" The pressure of the anger was building up inside, I felt desperate.

"Well just say to yourself, 'I'm going to be O.K.' Be positive for a change."

"Bloody positive! It's not in my mind you know!"

"Well stop acting as though it is then."

"What do you mean?" The dam inside strained to hold back the deluge of fury.

"Well," he mocked, "running out like that last night. People are going to think you're a nutter or something."

"I'm *not* a nutter," my voice was adamant and strong, "Simon says I'm not, so don't keep on calling me that!"

"Oh *I* see," his sarcasm cut like a knife. "If Simon says you're not, that's O.K. But *Simon* doesn't have to live with you, *I* do. It's the same thing, day in day out. I can't go out when I want, go to work when I want – everything I do has to revolve around you. All I want is to have a normal life, not this bloody crap!"

That did it – the dam burst. I lurched towards him, angry and hurt. Now the temper would erupt and I wouldn't be able to stop it.

"I *can't* help it, you fool!" I screamed, glaring at him. "Can't you understand that? If it was happening to *you*, then it would be a different story."

"You bet," he said, attempting a sneer, "I'd be different alright! For a start, I'd just get on with it instead of whingeing all the time."

"Oh, you're so clever, aren't you?" I hated him at that moment. "If you have just a little cold you do nothing but moan all the time!"

He walked towards the door. I watched him take his jacket from the hall cupboard. "Where are you going?" I demanded.

"Out. Away from you!"

"No!...No! You can't!" I was frightened now.

"Try and stop me and see what happens then," he threatened.

"No! No! Please!" I spread myself across the doorway blocking his path.

"Get away from there!" He pulled me across the hall, swinging me by my arm. The pain shot up to my neck.

"You pig! You bloody pig!" I began to cry – uncontrollable sobs that didn't seem to come from my body. He lunged forward, pushing me hard against the wall.

"You're evil, you are!" he hissed through his teeth. His face hard and set, was inches from mine. "You're a fucking evil bitch; why are you making my life hell? What have I done to deserve you?" He seized me by the shoulders and pushed me in front of the mirror. "Here, take a look at yourself – what do you see, eh?"

I stared at my reflection, but didn't speak. My breath was still stifled with sobs.

"I'll tell you what you see," he scorned. "A complete bastard – a complete *pathetic* bastard. You're a selfish bitch, only bothered about yourself and nobody else. Your friends can't be bothered with you, can they? Well neither can I. I'm sick of you!"

He let go of my shoulder and I sank down on the stairs – drained and beaten. "God, I want to die," I prayed. "Please let me die!"

"Will you stop bloody crying?" he shouted. "You're getting on my nerves. What's the matter with you? Why are you such a baby? You're not the girl I married, you're somebody else!"

I stared up at him, unable to recognise this person who towered above me. "I just want to die..." My voice was barely audible.

"Well, for God's sake go somewhere and die," he growled, "because I'm sick of hearing you say it. Do you hear me? *Sick!* You're driving me mad. The sooner I can get out of this bloody house the better, so you'd better go and find yourself another idiot to look after you. I don't want to know any more!"

He opened the door and, without looking back, walked out. This time I didn't try to stop him. I was too exhausted to fight any more.

I was now alone and very frightened. I reached for the telephone directory and began to look for the number of the city's largest psychiatric hospital. I needed to speak to someone – someone who would understand. My fingers shook clumsily as I dialled the number.

"St. Stephen's Hospital, can I help you?" The operator sounded cheerful and efficient.

I tried to make my voice sound as bright as hers. "I wonder if it is possible to have a word with Dr. Meredith, please?"

"Yes. Who shall I say is calling?"

"Heather Jones."

"One moment, I'll see if he's in his room."

The line went dead for a few moments.

"Oh. I hope he doesn't mind me calling him," I said to myself. Even though he had always said if I needed to speak to him between visits, I should phone, I still felt apprehensive.

"Hi, Heather, what can I do for you?" His warm and friendly tone told me there was no need to worry.

"I'm sorry to bother you, but..." my voice trailed off, lost for words. There was a brief silence.

"Is something the matter, Heather?" His concern immediately brought back the tears.

"I had to ring somebody," I said brushing the tears away with my thumb. "You see I've got no one to talk to, there's nobody here."

"Well how about talking to me?" His voice was gentle. "I'm here."

"Don't you mind though?" I asked. "It's just that I'm so frightened. I'll be O.K. if I can talk to someone for a while."

"No – I don't mind," he replied. "What's made you upset anyway?"

"Oh – you know, arguing with Lou and things."

"What do you mean – 'things'?"

"Oh, it's just that Paul was in a concert at school last night and I had to come home before it even began." I started to tell him about the previous night's events, but even as I spoke I found myself thinking, "Lou's right. I am pathetic. How could I have reacted like that if I wasn't?" Simon listened patiently, interrupting only to make the odd acknowledgement. When he was sure I had finished he spoke again, but this time his voice was firm.

"Well before we discuss anything, let's get one thing straight. You are *not* a 'nutter', so get that out of your head – right? Now the other thing is, how much Valium are you on now? 4 mg isn't it?"

"Yes, that's right, oh – and the odd Ativan sometimes at night. You don't think I should cut them down any more, do you?" I sounded worried.

"No – not at the moment. But how long have you been on that dose now?"

"About two months I think. Why do you ask?"

"Well, I don't want you to reduce any more, not for the time being anyway. O.K?"

"Right," I said relieved, "but why?"

"Well, I think you're in a very anxious state, and at the moment need some sort of sedation. We don't want what happened last night to happen again, do we?"

I agreed with him, greatly reassured: I *wasn't* going mad. Simon was always there if I needed him. And I could keep on taking my Valium...for a little while, anyway. These would help to stop these feelings – Simon had told me this.

* * * * *

I stayed on 4 mg for one year. It was a year of hell.

My body became weaker, my mind more tormented, and I rarely ventured outside. If it was really necessary to go out a Valium would save the day. Being on my own was now totally unthinkable. When Lou had to go out and Louise and Paul were not at home, he would call on friends or relations to 'baby-sit'. I tried to hide the humiliation of this by attempting to explain, but I knew they couldn't understand, tolerating me for a short while, and unable to hide their need to get away.

"I don't know what to suggest," Eileen spoke to Lou in a lowered voice.

"Well something will have to be done soon," he replied, "things can't go on like this."

I felt like an eavesdropper, sitting on the stairs listening in to a hushed conversation between my husband and friend. Lou had just returned home after being out for a few hours. Eileen had been keeping me company.

"I'm going to have a bath," I had told them, "I won't be long." But half-way up the stairs something had told me to stop. "They're talking about me," I thought, sitting quietly down on one of the steps.

I didn't want to hear what was being said, but I felt compelled to listen; as I sat, gulfs of despair began to envelop my body.

"Oh, I agree with you," Eileen continued, "the whole thing is ridiculous. I mean it isn't as though she is getting any better, is it? How long has she been seeing Simon now?"

"Oh – well over two years," Lou answered.

"And do you think he's doing her any good?"

"Well, in certain ways – yes, I think he is. I mean she had a lot of problems with her childhood, you know, and they seem to be alright now. But these fears she talks about, they seem to be worse if anything."

"Well, I don't know," remarked Eileen, "there doesn't seem to be an answer to it all, does there?"

"No, there doesn't," Lou's voice sounded flat, despondent.

"Are she and Joan speaking yet?"

My constant mood swings had finally upset Joan and for many months we had not been in touch. This had been a persistent thorn in my side – I still hated it if anyone thought ill of me – but a phone call had resolved this (her dog was having puppies and we offered to help). Yet again the bond that had been broken between us was healed, and I promised myself I would try hard to keep it that way, trying hard to fight the unreasonable behaviour and curb the irrational outbursts.

"Yes," Lou replied. "She rang Heather the other day. I think things are O.K. now."

"Oh well, that should please her, anyway."

"Yes it does, I just wish we could get the rest sorted out though."

"Of course you do. It's gone on far too long, hasn't it? You must be really fed up."

"Well, it's not really happening to me is it? I just wish I knew what to do to make her well."

"What do you think is the matter with her then?"

"I'm not really sure. I don't think it's physical though – it's got to be something to do with her mind."

"Yes, it does look like that, doesn't it?" There was a silence for a few moments. I stood up carefully so as not to make any noise and started to climb the stairs.

"It's a shame that this has had to happen now though," Eileen had begun to speak again. "I mean the kids aren't babies any more, they're grown up. You should be enjoying your-selves now, not going through this." I stopped stock-still, my hand clutching the bannister.

"Yes, I know." Lou's voice was now much quieter, and I detected a note of sadness.

"I mean, I feel sorry for you as well," Eileen continued. "It must be an awful strain."

Tears, a mixture of shame and anger, spilled down my cheeks. "How *dare* they talk about me like this. I *know* there is something wrong, but it *isn't* my mind!" Shame overpowered me, however. "They may have no right to speak about me like that – but that doesn't make them wrong!" I was a failure, a *complete* failure – to be discussed in hushed tones when I was out of the room.

*   *   *   *   *

As the year progressed – so did my deterioration; the physical and mental decline became so debilitating that I could fight it no longer. I had thought it impossible to feel any worse than I did, but I was wrong. Apart from all the old symptoms, many new ones had developed. My limbs were sore and heavy – sometimes feeling as though they were made of jelly – and I had no control over them; it became almost impossible to walk in a straight line. I suffered from blurred and double vision and, despite wearing dark glasses, my eyes were increasingly sensitive to light.

The abdominal cramps had now become so severe that the discomfort and pain alone completely overshadowed my life; because so many foods upset my digestive system, my diet became even more limited and the long-standing vitamin and mineral deficiency produced a rapid deterioration: I became very thin. Colic was now a major problem and, when combined with my persistent insomnia, nights became an ordeal. My G.P. prescribed several different anti-spasmodic drugs, but these had no beneficial effects whatsoever.

Nothing seemed to help any more. I could no longer eat, sleep or go out. I had turned into some form of monster, full of sickness, fear and anger – alien both to the people who knew me and to myself – a completely lost cause.

The 4 mg of Valium was no longer enough to live a normal life. I needed more.

APRIL 1983

I stood in the kitchen, frozen with fear, not knowing what to do. It was April 30th 1983, and I had in front of me an ordeal from which I couldn't back down.

"I don't know how I'm going to make it to this concert," I had told Lou the day before.

"Oh you will somehow," he had replied. "You won't be able to live with yourself if you don't."

My favourite singer, Johnny Mathis, was touring the country and we had managed to obtain four front row seats. Going to any concert would normally be a tremendous task, but this one was over 100 miles away, in Edinburgh, and the mere thought of it filled me with dread.

"I can't go!" I had cried. "It's too far!"

"Of course it's not," Lou had tried to reassure me. "It won't take long by car and it isn't as though you don't know the people you're going with. I mean I'll be with you and I'm sure everyone will understand if you feel ill." Lou wasn't going to the concert but he had said he would act as chauffeur, driving us there and back. "Anyway, if you don't go, you will let all the others down."

This was true. 'The others' – Loreen, a neighbour, pen-pal Danièle and Joan – were all personal friends, knowing each other only slightly. If I didn't go – they couldn't go.

"I mean, Danièle has probably got her rail ticket by now," Lou had continued. Danièle lived in my old home town of Hull which meant she would have to travel from there to Newcastle on the day of the concert.

Yes, Lou was right. By not going I would let everybody down, and at the same time lose the small trace of self-respect that I had left. Somehow, I had to make it.

The familiar fear now ran rife through my body, turning everything over inside. "Oh, please God, let me be alright," I silently prayed. My heart banged so loud against my chest, it took my breath away. I still didn't know how to handle these feelings – it was as though an unknown force took over from within, overriding any will-power that I might have left with which to combat it.

"It's no good," I thought frantically, "I can't stand this! I'll have to tell them I can't go." My friends had by now arrived and were gathered in the lounge, laughing and joking with each other.

"I hope he sings more of his old hits," Loreen was saying. "Last time he sang a lot of new ones."

"He can sing nursery rhymes for all I care," laughed Danièle, "he'd still sound good to me!"

"I'm pleased we've got such good seats – right in the middle of the front row," said Loreen, "at least we'll have a good view."

"You watch," Joan remarked light-heartedly, "knowing my luck, I'll probably get stuck behind the conductor or something!"

I stood in the kitchen, frozen to the spot. "Oh dear God," I said to myself, "what am I to do? I can't let them down, not now!"

There was only one thing to do. I opened the cupboard door and reach for the familiar brown bottle. I shook out three small white tablets into the palm of my hand. "That's two...four...six milligrams," I counted silently to myself, closing my eyes slowly. "Please let me be doing the right thing." Without a second thought, I swallowed them. Ten minutes later the Valium did all that it was supposed to, and I felt great!

We took the scenic route to Edinburgh, taking in all the rugged but beautiful landscape. Magnificent tree-clad hills rolled down into green and golden fields, where spring lambs frolicked around their mothers. Small rivers meandered slowly through lush valleys, sparkling in the warm sunlight. It was a beautiful day – no fear, no anxiety – just warmth, tranquillity and Johnny Mathis!

Driving home that night, I felt at peace with the world. The journeys had been relaxed and easy, and the company happy and friendly. Johnny had looked and sounded great and, last but not least, I had made it! The Valium had done its job, and I was master of my body once more.

*   *   *   *   *

I sat on the edge of the bed and stared up at Lou. Two days had now passed since the concert, and the warm relaxed contentment that had been mine for a day had now totally fled. The old fears had rebounded with an inconsolable fury. I was confused and desperately frightened.

He towered over me, cold and angry. "What the hell is the matter with you?" he muttered. "I just can't make you out – you're like two different people. One day, quite normal, and then the next...you've turned into this shrivelling mess. It's about time you grew up!"

The grief engulfed me and I slipped off the bed onto the floor. Sobbing loudly. "Oh shut up, will you!" He bent down and grabbed a hold of my arm, twisting it up my back. "I can't stand this any more do you hear! Just bloody shut up!" The pain in my arm caused me to cry out more. "I've warned you," he continued, menacingly, "I've had enough. If you don't pull yourself together, I'll bugger off for good – right?"

This caused the sobs to come even louder – deep and insistent. Suddenly, his hand came down hard across the side of my face, shocking me into silence.

Eventually I found my voice. "Leave me alone!" I half-whispered, and he slowly released his hold on me. I pulled myself free, and crawled across the floor away from him, huddling myself into the corner of the room. I pulled my knees up under my chin and wrapped my arms tightly around them.

"Why are you so cruel?" I whispered, my breath stifled with sobs.

"Me? Cruel?" he exclaimed. "You're the one who is bloody cruel, not me – putting me through this fucking hell every day. All *you* can think about is yourself!"

I pressed myself harder into the corner, the two walls feeling like an embrace. There was a terrific pressure inside my head, and my thoughts – all jumbled up inside – screamed to be let out. "Please...someone help me..." I begged softly.

Lou hesitated for a moment then hurried over to me. He leaned over me, his hands touching my shoulders, more gently this time, and stroked the hair away from my face. I peered up at him through swollen eyes. Seconds earlier, anger and frustration had changed this gentle giant into a violent, aggressive monster. I cowered, bewildered and alarmed.

"Oh, Heather," he said, his voice now soft with concern, "what's the matter with you? You were alright when we went to Edinburgh. What's gone wrong?"

I looked at him, unable to explain. The pressure inside my head became more intense. I began to trace the flowers on the wallpaper with my index finger. "Now I'm going mad!" I thought. "Let them take me away, I don't care any more."

He looked at me with astonishment and disbelief. "Come on love, don't do that," he crouched down next to me, putting his arm around my shoulders, his tone much softer. "I'm sorry I hit you, I really am. I didn't mean to, you know, it's just that it's all so frustrating at times and I'm so worried about you. I *hate* seeing you like this, but I don't know what to do. I just want you to get well." I glanced at his face and noticed how pale and drawn he looked.

"Please get me some help," I begged, "I think I'm going mad."

"Do you want me to phone and ask if Simon can see you?" he asked.

I nodded hurriedly – the fear overwhelming – I had to have help.

"Well come on then," he coaxed, "let's go downstairs and I'll ring him for you."

One hour later we pulled up outside the Grainger Clinic, an annexe of the hospital where Simon now worked. "I don't want you to bring her here," he had told Lou on the phone, "it's not very suitable." He was talking about St. Stephen's, the city's main psychiatric hospital where he had then worked for some time. Most of the patients there were long term – some would be in for most of their lives. "Let me see – do you know how to get to the Grainger Clinic?"

"I'm not quite sure," Lou had replied, "but I'm sure I'll be able to find it."

"Well, it's the first turning left after the main hospital entrance. I think I know of a room that will be vacant."

We had found the clinic with no problem at all. It was a grey single-storey building set apart from the hospital itself. I had heard that the patients here were usually short-stay ones – the really bad cases were admitted to St. Stephen's. It was then as we walked up to the entrance that the fear began to subside. This was typical of the way it would be – coming in waves, rising and abating, constricting and releasing – and I never knew how long each wave would last.

The foyer of the clinic was brightly painted with pictures and posters adorning the walls. It reminded me of the infant school Louise and Paul had attended. Several young people walked by in a group, headed by a young man in his early twenties. He wore no uniform – just jeans and a sweatshirt – and as he passed where we were standing, he stopped and turned round.

"Are you looking for someone?" he asked, walking over. The name-tag pinned on his shirt read *Peter Turner. Charge Nurse.*

"Yes, Dr. Meredith told us to meet him here at about two-thirty," Lou replied. The nurse looked at me more closely. "Are you Heather Jones?" he asked, and I nodded in reply. "Well he rang about half an hour ago to say he was coming over. In fact, if you'd like to take a seat in here for a few minutes I'll go and chase him up for you." He gestured towards a doorway just in front of him.

"Thanks very much," said Lou, and we followed the little troop into a large room. High-backed seats were placed all the way around the parquet floor. There was no other furniture.

"I wonder if this is where they hold their dances?" Lou whispered to me jokingly, as we sat down. I smiled and nodded.

The Charge Nurse was busy allotting his little brood in to different seats. "John, can you sit there, and Jean and Ruth keep an eye on Martin for me, will you? I won't be a moment." He smiled at Lou and I as he left the room. As the patients began to chatter amongst themselves one of them, a youth aged about eighteen, hovered around one of the chairs.

"I'm *not* sitting there!" he declared, pointing at the seat.

"Oh, come on Martin," the girl whom the charge nurse had referred to as Ruth walked over, "what's the matter?"

"It's *that* chair. I don't like it!" he said, glaring at the offending item.

"What's the matter with it?" asked the girl.

"Well, it's orange," he announced as though it was obvious. "I don't like orange."

Lou looked at me sideways, not saying a word. I shrank down under the collar of my jacket. "Oh, dear Jesus," I thought, "the poor boy. But please don't let me be like that. I couldn't stand it if I was like that!" At that moment the Charge Nurse came back into the room.

"Peter – it's Martin," said the girl called Jean. "He's being difficult again."

"Oh dear," the nurse shook his head with a smile. "What on earth are we going to do with you, eh?" He took the young boy gently by his arm, and turned to Lou and I. "If you'd like to go to the room at the end of the corridor, Dr. Meredith is waiting for you. Sorry I can't take you, but I'd better stop here. Do you mind?"

"No, that's O.K.," said Lou, and we left the room and walked along the long hall. As we neared the end, Simon popped his head around an open door-way.

"Ah – Heather – Lou, come on in. I see you found us O.K?"

"No problem." Lou replied, sitting down on one of the two seats in front of the desk. I sat down on the other. There were no other chairs in the room. Simon perched himself against the desk, half-sitting, half-standing, arms folded across his chest.

"Well, what seems to be the matter?" he asked.

"It's Heather," Lou said, "she says she can't go on any more."

Simon looked down at me. "And what's been happening to you?" he said, frowning concernedly.

I began to relate to him the happenings of the last few days, starting with the build-up to the concert. I described how I had had to increase the amount of Valium I was taking in order to get there, and how I now felt, after the effects of the drug had worn off. He listened carefully to what I had to say, biting gently on his knuckles as I spoke.

"Let me see," he frowned again, thoughtfully. "You say you took 6 mg extra two days ago – that makes 8 mg altogether – and you said you were alright until this morning?"

"That's right," I said. "I wasn't too bad yesterday, but today I feel really awful. It's this fear – it keeps coming and going without any warning – and I'm so depressed."

"More depressed than usual?" he asked.

I nodded slowly. "Yes – you know I think I'd rather be dead than live like this." He gave a small, sad smile, but didn't speak.

"Something will have to be done," Lou broke into the conversation. "She can't keep on like this."

"Yes, I know," Simon agreed with him, "but *what* to do is the problem. Anyway," he said turning to me, "I'm pleased that you went to the concert – that was a good thing that you did – but this depression that you're feeling now is probably due to all the added stress you had to go through to get there. One usually follows the other..." He paused before speaking again, "I know I've always been against you taking drugs, but how would you feel if we changed your tranquilliser?"

"How do you mean – stop the Valium and Ativan?"

"Yes," he replied. "You see sometimes if you take a drug for a long time your body becomes use to it, so it no longer does it's job properly. That's why I'd like you to change to a different one and see if that helps."

"A different one?" I was instantly suspicious.

"Yes, that's right. Well, it's in the same family as Valium, but it varies slightly in make-up."

"I see," I said, "but will there any awful side-effects from them?"

"No – you'll probably feel a bit better if anything," he replied. "So what do you think? Do you want to give it a try?" I looked at Lou, who nodded in agreement.

"Alright then," I said. "I'll try them and see. What are they called?"

"I was thinking of trying you on Oxazepam – Serenid-D." He searched into his inside pocket and took out a pen. "Now let me see if I can find a prescription form – there's usually one around here somewhere."

As he searched through the drawer of the desk, I glanced over to Lou. The smile he gave me was one of hope and relief. "Come on love, don't worry," it seemed to say, "you're going to be alright – just wait and see."

And once again we left the hospital with hope in our hearts and a prescription in our hands. But yet again the hope was to be short lived...

Serenid and I never became compatible. Within fifteen minutes of taking one I would feel much better, but this feeling would soon wear off, bringing back all the old symptoms with a vengeance. To stop this from happening they had to be taken a lot more frequently than Valium – something I was very reluctant to do.

"I've got to take far more of these to feel O.K." I told Lou. "They only seem to work for a few hours and when they wear off it's terrible."

"Well why don't you take more?" he suggested.

"Because just taking more pills seems like a step in the wrong direction."

Lou sighed. "How do you expect to get anywhere if you don't do as the doctors tell you?"

But I was insistent. "I just don't want to increase the amount of pills I'm taking – can't you understand? I'd rather just go back onto Valium – at least with those the feelings were steady all day – but with Serenid, the one I take at breakfast has worn off by the afternoon."

Lou wasn't very pleased. "Well you'll have to mention it to Simon the next time you see him," he said.

So a week later I stopped taking Serenid and went back onto Valium.

During the weeks of taking the new drug nothing had improved in any way. It's effects had worn off so quickly that life under its influence had swung between a few hours of heaven and even more hours of hell. Life back on Valium, however, was just a steady purgatory in which suicidal thoughts were never far away.

I knew I had reached breaking point. If I wanted to survive *something* would have to change. I knew in my heart that I could not go on like this any longer.

June 1983

It was several days after seeing the article in the local paper that I decided to do something about it. "When The Tranquillisers Stop," the headline to the article had read. It told the story of a young housewife addicted to tranquillisers for seven years who had, in common with many others, suffered terrible physical and mental symptoms when withdrawing from the drug. I had torn the article out of the newspaper and pushed it into a drawer.

While half of my brain was still too depressed to want to be bothered with yet another false hope, the other half of me – the sensible part – somehow wouldn't let go of the idea. "Maybe this is what is wrong with me?" it kept saying, and nagged and nagged me to take heed of what the article had said. Three days later, the sensible half won. "It has to be worth a try," I thought in desperation, "because if I don't get help soon I think I will die."

The article mentioned the telephone number of a self-help group that had been set up in a small terrace house in the East end of the city. It was here that people who were having problems withdrawing from tranquillisers could go to get support.

The girl who answered the phone sounded bright and friendly. "Hello, Tranquilliser Support Group."

"I...I wonder if you can help me at all?" my voice was apprehensive. "I've just read your article in the Chronicle and it mentions that you have started a group to help people who are coming off tranquillisers?"

"Yes, that's right," she replied.

"Well – I've been on Valium for quite a long time now, and I've been cutting down for three years. But I feel so ill now I don't know what to do."

"You're not off them completely?" she asked.

"No – I'm down to 4 mg. You see my doctor told me not to cut down any more until I felt better. Well that was over a year ago now and the trouble is I'm getting worse."

"Well you probably would be," she replied, "because you'll be getting withdrawal symptoms on that low dose."

"Withdrawal symptoms?"

"Yes. When your body has been used to a higher dose, it starts to complain loudly when you cut it down."

I could hardly believe what I was hearing. "So you reckon all these fears I'm having are to do with withdrawal?"

"Yes, I'm sure they are. Fear and panic are very common symptoms. Lots of people get them. In fact I know exactly what they're like because it has happened to me."

"You're on tranquillisers?"

"No – not any more. I came off them about two months ago. But I do know how you're feeling."

"Were you frightened of going out?"

"Goodness – yes. In fact I still am a bit but I'm not half as bad as I was; for instance I came here this morning – admittedly in a taxi – but even that was something I couldn't have done a month ago."

I was so excited I could hardly get my words out fast enough. "But what about everything else? Do you think that the dizziness and blurred vision are to do with cutting down as well?"

"I'm sure they are."

"The depression and the insomnia?"

"Definitely."

"And my tummy problems – they're dreadful," I continued, "and I'm terrified of being left on my own."

"Honestly, these are all classic withdrawal symptoms. Listen, why don't you come along and meet us all? I'm sure you'll benefit from it."

But of course there was still one problem. "It...it might be a bit difficult getting there. You see – I have agoraphobia."

"Don't let that worry you," she sounded reassuring, "most of the people who come here have the same problem. By the way, I'm Tina, you didn't mention your name."

"Heather – Heather Jones. If I do come do I ask for you?"

"Oh no – I just help out. It's Fay Benedict who you need to see. She's a nursing sister and she's the one who started the group. But don't worry, she's very nice and she'll understand everything you're going through, because she's been through it herself."

My hopes were beginning to rise once more. "When are you open?"

"Tuesday evening from seven o'clock, and every Wednesday and Thursday afternoon. Look – shall I tell Fay to expect you? It's just that she likes to have a little talk with you on your own first."

"Yes, that's fine. By the way, is it okay if I bring my husband?"

"Of course it is," she replied. "He'll be able to talk to other wives and husbands – sometimes this helps them to understand. Do you know where to find us?"

"Yes. The article said it was 132 Tranby Terrace."

"That's right. So I'll look forward to meeting you soon." I thanked her very much for her help and put the phone down.

I felt delirious with happiness. It was as though a great weight had been lifted from my body and my mind. I couldn't wait to tell Lou; to tell the kids; to tell everybody.

It *wasn't* me after all. It was the *drugs!*

*   *   *   *   *

It was seven o'clock on the following Tuesday evening when we turned the car into Tranby Terrace. It was raining hard and the steady monotonous swish of the windscreen wipers seemed to steady the uneasiness in my stomach. Lou drove slowly, counting the numbers on the houses as we passed.

"One hundred and twenty – twenty two. It must be somewhere near here," he said.

"That must be it," I said, pointing to a brightly-lit terrace house on the corner of the street. It stood out from the rest of the houses: vertical blinds hung at the windows which were larger and more modern-looking than the others, and the door, which was on the side of the building, was painted bright red. It appeared to have once been a shop. The rain beat down on our heads as we left the car and hurried up to the door. I knocked tentatively.

"Come on in," a man's voice boomed cheerfully from inside.

We walked straight into a large pleasant room in which many chairs were lined up against the walls and several more, stacked one on top of each other, filled a far corner. There was a large table opposite, on which sat a telephone and typewriter, and it was here that two dark-haired young men, one bearded, the other clean-shaven, sat talking to a small thin-faced older man. In the other corner a small plump woman of about sixty, was washing some cups in the sink.

"You can never find a clean cup in this place," she grumbled good-naturedly, and her rounded features broke into a broad smile.

"Hello there!" she said. "Don't mind me – I just like to moan a bit now and then. This is your first time here isn't it? – I'm Sadie by the way."

I smiled at her. "Yes it is. I've come to see someone called Fay Benedict about coming off tranquillisers.

"Yes – that's right," she said. "She's in the office at the moment. She shouldn't be long, take a seat for a moment."

As we sat down, I glanced around nervously, half wishing I hadn't come. "Don't look so worried – we're all friends here," the bearded man spoke again. "I'm Pat, by the way, and this is John and Frank." The other two men nodded in acknowledgement. "And this is Sadie," he said, smiling at the plump woman who had first greeted me.

"Hello," I smiled at them, relaxing slightly. "I'm Heather Jones and this is my husband, Lou."

"It's good that you have come along too," Pat nodded across to Lou. "It'll help you to understand. I know that my wife can cope a lot better since she has been coming here."

"Well I hope so," replied Lou. "I'm not doing very well at the moment."

"Most husbands and wives feel like that at first," said Pat. "Once they understand about withdrawal, everything becomes easier."

"Have you spoken to someone on the phone?" asked Sadie.

"Yes. Somebody called Tina."

"Ah, yes," she said, "I wonder where she is? She's usually here by now."

The older man who had been introduced as Frank, stood up and walked to the window. "Most people are usually here by now," he remarked, "It must be the weather – it's blooming awful out there!"

"He's right," Sadie agreed. "It's usually packed out by now. You've got to get here early to get a seat, haven't you Pat?"

"That's true," answered Pat. "Mind you some of them might not know Fay's back from her holiday." He turned to me again. "Are you still taking tranquillisers?" he said.

"Er...yes," I replied. "But I've cut right down."

"What are you on?"

"Valium. 4 mg now. I used to be on 15 mg though."

"You'll be feeling pretty rough at the moment, then?"

"Yes – I do a bit. This is what is worrying me – I mean, feeling like this and ill all the time."

"You'll feel a lot better when you're off completely," stated Sadie. "Being on that small dose nearly killed me."

"I've been on it for nearly a year now," I said.

"What!" exclaimed Pat. "That's a long time. What made you stop cutting down?"

"My doctor told me to stop at that dose as I felt so ill and he didn't want me to get any more anxious than I already was."

Pat shook his head in amazement. "You should ask to be referred to the one who helped me to come off, she's marvellous."

"What is her name?" I enquired.

"Helen Carlisle – she's a Senior Lecturer at the Blackwell Unit."

"I've never heard of that – where is it?"

"It's the Department of Pharmacological Sciences in the University Medical School; it's just behind the Royal Infirmary."

"That must be near Clayton Hall, then?" I said. "I used to see my doctor there."

"Yes, that's right," replied Pat. "They're next door to each other. You should really try and see her if you can, because honestly, if I hadn't, I think I would be insane by now."

"How long have you been off?" I asked him.

"Thirteen weeks," he said proudly.

"And you feel O.K?"

"Well...I'm a lot *better!* In fact, compared to what I was – bloody marvellous! If you had seen me six months ago, you would know what I mean."

"Were you on Valium?"

"No – Ativan. But Helen Carlisle put me onto Valium when I was cutting down."

"How long did you take them for?"

"Three years. I was given them in an attempt to help my tinnitus – you know, ringing in the ears – and they worked at first, but after a while the noises got worse so the doctor put the dose up. Then I developed these pains in my head; it was as though there was a steel band round my skull and someone was tightening it with a key. I was convinced I had a brain tumour and kept going back to the doctor who said it was caused by just about *everything* except the drugs. I knew I shouldn't be taking so many, but I really thought I needed them.

"I tried cutting down myself, but in the end I couldn't stand it any more. That's when I came here, and Fay put me in touch with Dr. Carlisle. Since then I've never looked back. Mind you it hasn't been easy with the depression and all the fears."

"You had fears?" I asked, amazed that this confident young man was frightened in any way at all. He seemed so sure of himself.

"Good God, yes!" he exclaimed. "I used to leap out of bed at two in the morning and run round the house in a blind panic, crying like a baby. It was terrible – and as for the agoraphobia...well, the only thing that kept me going was this group. That, and knowing that everything would be O.K. in the end. Mind you, my wife was marvellous. How she stayed with me I'll never know."

"I think she needs a medal to have put up with you," chuckled Sadie.

I smiled at her. "Are you off as well?" I was astonished at the confidence of these people. "Will I ever be like them?" I said to myself.

"Yes," she answered. "Valium – three months ago like Pat. Mind you, my problem was noise – I was just so sensitive to it. I couldn't even stand cleaning my teeth: I had to put toothpaste on some tissue paper and rub them gently."

At that moment, a door opened at the end of the room and a short, middle-aged brunette dressed in a smart grey suit came in. "This must be Fay Benedict," I thought.

"Hello, everybody." She looked around, smiling brightly. "My, we are a small lot tonight, aren't we? Her eyes rested on Lou and I. "Ah, two new faces. Have you all been introduced?"

"Yes, they've had that pleasure," Pat announced and grinned.

"Take no notice of him," laughed Fay. "Are you both together?"

"Yes," replied Lou. "Actually, I've just come along to keep my wife company, if that's O.K.?"

"Sure. I'd like to have a quick word with you both first though. Would you like to come through into the other room for a moment?"

We followed Fay out of the room down a short internal hall, which led to another room at the rear of the house. She sat down in front of a large desk and beckoned us to sit on a small settee opposite her.

"Now let's see," she said turning her chair around so she faced us. "So this is your first visit here?"

"Yes, that's right," I replied. "I rang last Thursday and the girl on the phone told me to come along."

"Ah yes, that would be Tina — I think she did mention something." She picked up a black book that lay open on the desk and began to turn back the pages. I watched her as she read. Her brown shoulder-length hair was parted in the middle, and she frequently had to brush it behind her ears.

"Oh, yes, here we are," she said pointing her pen at an entry in the book. "Heather Jones, isn't it?"

I nodded, "Yes, and this is my husband, Lou."

"I'm glad you came along too," she smiled at him, "you'll find it helps. Now Heather, it says here that you are having trouble coming off Valium?"

"Yes, that's right. I'm down to 4 mg now and I feel pretty awful." I began to unfold to her the story of my decline over the past few years. She listened carefully to what I had to say, peering at me through her hair.

"I see," she said when I had finished. "You say that you've been cutting down for about three years now?"

"Yes — that's right."

"Well in my opinion that is rather a long time. Cutting down too quickly is not advisable, but neither is dragging the process out: it turns the whole thing into a long debilitating illness which makes you feel very run down and weak. I think that this is what has happened to you: not only have you been suffering for a long time from the drug's side-effects, but you're also, without realising it, in withdrawal." I must have looked a bit puzzled, so Fay smiled. "Let me explain. When you consider what the drugs do — how they control anxiety, slow down your heart rate, relax your muscles and help you to sleep — it's understandable that when you cut down or stop the drug you will get a rebound reaction. It's a bit like taking the top off a Jack-in-the-Box."

"So all these awful symptoms have been from drug side-effects and withdrawal at the same time?" I asked her.

"Yes — that's right."

"So the agoraphobia and the temper outbursts — which ones are they?"

"Possibly both," she said. "You see the drugs suffocate the emotions so that when your body becomes used to taking them, or you withdraw them, you can become temporarily aggressive and hard to live with." She smiled at Lou. "I know it is difficult for you and your family, but don't worry, your emotions will return to normal again when *you* control your feelings, not the drugs." She turned again to Lou. "How are you coping with all this? I bet you're pretty sick of it all, aren't you?"

He took a deep breath and blew out slowly. "Well, some days are worse than others," he replied. "I must admit, though, sometimes I haven't been as patient with her as I should have been. I tend to lose my temper a lot more these days."

"I'm sure by coming to the group it will help you to understand more of what's happening and thereby better able to cope!" Fay told him.

"I hope so," he replied.

"Lou has had to give his job up to look after me," I said to her. "I feel very guilty about that."

"Well don't," she gently admonished. "This happens to lots of people. I mean if you had pneumonia or a broken leg would you feel guilty then, would you?" I shook my head. "Well try to say to yourself, 'I've nothing to feel guilty about; I've been ill for a long time and I temporarily need help in order to get better'."

I took a deep breath. "Do you think I should come off these 4 mg then?" I asked her.

"Well, they certainly aren't doing you any good – so, *I* would say come off them, but make sure you discuss it with your doctor first – Dr. Meredith, you say his name is?"

"Yes, that's right," I replied. "But what about this other doctor – Helen Carlisle? Pat says she is good."

"She is – very good. So why don't you ask your Dr. Meredith if you can be referred to her?"

"Yes, I'll do that," I said excitedly. "I'm seeing him tomorrow, so I'll ask him then."

"Good," she smiled. "In the meantime I'll give you a diet sheet that might help you to feel better."

"Diet sheet?"

"Yes – you see one side-effect of the drug is that it artificially lowers your blood sugar level and therefore hypoglycaemia is very common in withdrawal." She saw my worried expression. "But don't worry – again, this is only temporary, and this diet sheet is only a guide line to try and help you to keep your blood-sugar level normal. This, and all the other symptoms, will gradually pass in time, just you wait and see."

"Do you really think so?"

"Yes, I honestly do. I'm sure once you come off the drugs completely, the depression, the fears, the insomnia and all your tummy problems will all improve. I know mine did." She glanced at her watch. "Now then, how would you like it if we went and joined the others for a cup of tea? There will probably be more here by now."

As we stood up to leave the room she put her hand on my shoulder.

"Don't you worry, now," she said kindly, "things have been pretty rough, but they're going to get better. Just keep on telling yourself this – because it is true."

As the three of us walked back into the other room I felt a sense of exhilaration. I *believed* what Fay had said and this time I *knew* – not just hoped – but *knew* that I had found the answer at last!

July 1983

For the first time in three years, Simon Meredith was angry with me. I had hardly been able to contain my excitement since I had left the group the night before and had phoned everybody I could – all our friends and relations – to tell them that it was the *drugs* that had been destroying my life, not me, and that by withdrawing them properly I would be able to return to normal once more. Everybody had been so thrilled.

Everybody, that is, except Simon.

I was full of eager enthusiasm as I chattered to him about the findings of the previous night. He listened quietly, his lips compressed into a thin, controlled line. After a brief silence he spoke. "I see," he said, his dark quiet eyes belying the coldness in his voice, "so you believe these people, whom you've only met for a couple of hours or so, instead of believing me?"

"No, no!" I tried to explain. "It's not like that. It's just that they've all had my symptoms, and since they stopped taking tranquillisers, they all seem to be a lot better."

"Hmm," he leant back on his chair, frowning slightly. "So what you're saying is that all your fears and depressions are really withdrawal symptoms?"

"Yes, but the symptoms can be from both withdrawal and drug side-effects, especially if you've been taking tranquillisers for a long time."

Simon looked sceptical and shook his head. "I wouldn't be too sure about that. These drugs have been out for a long time you know, so I think if there was something so drastically wrong with them, we'd have heard about it by now."

I stood my ground. "Well, maybe doctors don't realise that it's the drugs that are making people ill."

"On the contrary, doctors *do* expect some withdrawal symptoms – but nothing as extreme as the ones you describe."

"What sort of symptoms do they expect, then?"

"Oh. A little bit of anxiety and feeling uptight for a few days; maybe even a little difficulty in sleeping – but nothing to worry about."

I thought for a few moments before answering. I had always believed in what Simon had said – trusting completely in everything he told me over the past three years. But now I had to disagree; a deep intuition told me so.

"Honestly, Simon," I persisted, "I don't agree. I mean, it's just too much of a coincidence that all those people had had the same symptoms as myself. And another thing – I don't believe it is my old anxiety coming back again, because I *know* I never felt like this before I took tranquillisers, and all the others at the group say it had been the same for them too. Anyway, one man there hadn't been prescribed tranquillisers for psychological reasons at all: he had had a muscular injury in his knee and now, after taking Valium to help it, he has exactly the same symptoms as the rest of us. He can't sleep or stay on his own and has developed agoraphobia; considering that he used to be a very fit footballer, you can imagine he feels rather bitter about it all now."

I paused for a few moments, waiting for his reaction. It took a little time, but eventually he gave me a doubtful smile.

"Well Heather, you seem pretty adamant that this is what is wrong with you – so I won't argue. As I've always said, it is up to *you* to make the decisions in your life; all I've ever tried to do is guide you in the right direction."

I was prepared for this. I knew Simon had always acted with the best of intentions and had only ever been concerned about my well-being. "I know that, Simon. And I'm not trying to belittle the help you have given me over the last three years..." then I took a deep breath. I had come here for a purpose. "But, please...*please* can I see this Doctor Carlisle?" I looked at him with pleading in my eyes, "I mean it has got to be worth at least a try, hasn't it?"

He nodded slowly. "Well, if that's what you really want, that's what you shall have. It might take a few weeks – depending on whether she has a waiting list or not – but I'll get in touch with her for you immediately."

I sank back into my chair, relieved.

I knew Simon was still not very pleased and this concerned me – I really did not want to upset him. But at the same time I had to follow my instinct – the instinct to survive. This told me that I needed to go and see Dr. Carlisle and to carry on attending the group. There there were people I could associate with, people with whom I felt completely at ease; people who, on the face of it, were all very different, but who had been brought together by one common denominator – TRANQUILLISERS.

*   *   *   *   *

The following Tuesday, Lou and I returned to Tranby Terrace. This time I felt no uneasiness, and we took our seats beside all the people who had been there the previous week. This time there were some faces I didn't recognise from my last visit – but the welcome was just as warm as before.

"Ah, Heather and Lou," Pat greeted us from across the room. "Glad to see you again. As you can see, there are a few more of us here this week."

I smiled and nodded, glancing around the room quickly, trying to take in as many faces as possible. My gaze stopped on Sadie.

"Hello, pet," she said warmly as her plump pink cheeks creased into a smile. "How are you?"

"Oh, not so bad," I replied as we both sat down, "just waiting to go to the hospital to see Helen Carlisle."

"Ah – did you get an appointment with her?" asked Pat.

"My doctor is arranging it," I told him. "He's not very happy about it though." I felt I ought to defend Simon, "I mean, it's not that he *likes* prescribing tranquillisers, it's just that he does not believe that the symptoms I have been suffering from have been *caused* by them."

"My doctor was exactly the same," chipped in a bright, well-dressed red-head sitting next to Lou. "I was addicted to Valium for ten years without realising it, and my doctor just told me I was anxious and depressed and therefore needed them. I did not consider myself to be an anxious person, but because I felt so ill if I didn't take them, I thought he must be right."

"Did you feel ill when you were on them?" I asked, turning to her.

"Not at first. I was prescribed them for back-ache and I felt fine for months. It wasn't until I went to the Middle East – my first husband was working there at the time – that I had problems."

"What happened?"

"I decided I didn't want to take them any more so I flushed them down the toilet. Within five days I was in hospital on a drip-feed. The doctors over there had no idea what was wrong with me so I had to be flown home. I was put back onto Valium and immediately felt better. I even went through a divorce and didn't feel a thing!" she laughed.

"They certainly seem to block out all your emotions don't they?" I said to her. "Are you still taking them?"

"Not Valium – no," she answered. "I was put onto Ativan instead."

"Why was that?"

"Well, I re-married three years ago and thought it was time to stop taking the tablets! So I did – and on the third day, I collapsed again. This time I had an epileptic fit and the doctors thought I might have a brain tumour. Nobody suspected drug withdrawal – I even lost my Driving Licence because of the suspected fit – and I felt so ill at the time that they decided to put me on Ativan. That's when the most dreadful side effects came. My whole personality changed, my hair began to fall out, I developed headaches, toothache, back ache and had these terrible outbursts of temper and rage."

"I certainly know what you mean about those," I interrupted. "You feel as though your body has been taken over."

"That's right," she said nodding her head. "By the way, I haven't introduced myself – I'm Connie. You're Heather, aren't you?"

I nodded and smiled in acknowledgement. "Are you still on Ativan?" I asked her.

"Yes – but I'm waiting to go into hospital to come off them."

"Oh, you're going into hospital? I don't like the sound of that!"

"Well, I have to," she explained, "because I've nobody to look after me at home. My second husband left because he couldn't stand me being ill all the time, and even though I've got two teenage sons at home, I think it's too much responsibility for them to take." At that moment Fay Benedict entered the room.

"Hello there," she smiled at everyone and sat down on a chair next to the large table, her eyes resting on an elderly couple.

"Ah, Betty and Walter – how are you doing?"

Betty, a stout jolly-looking woman, smiled back. "Not so bad, thanks Fay," she replied.

"She is doing very well," piped in Walter, a distinguished-looking, grey-haired gentleman, whom I presumed to be her husband. "We've even booked a holiday in Austria for a few days next month."

"That's marvellous news!" Fay exclaimed. "It's really amazing how Betty has improved in six months, isn't it Walter? I mean there are quite a few people here who did not see her before she came off tranquillisers."

"That's right," Walter told the group, "she's like a different person. It had got so bad that she couldn't even hold a knife and fork. I had to spoon-feed her all her meals."

"I don't know what I would have done without him," smiled Betty, gently patting his hand. As she spoke a middle-aged couple entered the room.

"Enid, Sam – Hi," called Fay from across the room. "Are you on your own tonight?"

"No, we've come with Marie and Ken," said Enid, and as she spoke a short brunette in her mid-thirties, walked slowly into the room. A sturdily-built, slightly older man followed close behind her.

"Hi!" said Marie with just a hint of a smile on her face. It was as though she knew something amusing and was keeping it to herself. "Better late than never, I suppose." She sat herself down on the chair next to mine.

"Now then, Marie – how are you?" asked Fay.

"Well, I've made it here," she replied. The quizzical smile was still there. "In spirit, anyway. I think I've left my body in the car!" Her voice was deep and soft and as I looked at her I felt an instant amity: she wore very little make-up on her pretty face, and her bright alert eyes shone from round rosy cheeks. She wore her long heavy hair in a Fifties style.

Fay glanced around the room. "I want everyone to know – who doesn't already – that Marie came off her drugs 'cold turkey' – a way that is *not* recommended!"

"That's right," agreed Marie. "*Definitely* not recommended."

"I can second that," Enid broke in. "It nearly killed me when I did it."

"What made you do it?" asked Pat, his question directed at Enid.

"I don't really know," she replied. "I was just sick of feeling ill all the time and the doctors not knowing what was wrong. One day I just threw them away. I thought 'that's it, I don't need them any more!' You know at first I felt marvellous – completely lucid. I remember thinking – 'Great! I've cracked it!' Then on the third day it hit me like a hammer – all I could do was crawl around the flat all day and wait for Sam to come home."

"I thought she'd gone mad," Sam told us. "Nobody knew what was the matter. The doctors we saw didn't recognise that it was withdrawal, and all they wanted to do was to commit her to hospital."

"I got this awful pain in my jaw," Enid continued. "In fact I had to beg a dentist to take my teeth out it was so bad. It really makes me mad when I think of the twenty-eight perfectly healthy teeth I lost because of those drugs!"

"I used to rinse my mouth with whisky," Sadie broke in. "I found that helped a bit."

"That's the best excuse I have heard yet," laughed Pat.

"No – Sadie's right," Fay said with a smile. "Sucking an ice-cube can help as well, or having your neck massaged." She paused for a moment and peered around the room. "Now then, let's see how everyone has been getting on. I hope some of you have some good news this week."

"Well, I have volunteered for a charity parachute jump," Pat announced proudly.

"Really?" Fay sounded amazed. "That is excellent – I mean even under normal circumstances that is quite an achievement. You'll be having proper training I assume?"

"Of course," he said. "I couldn't do it otherwise. But I'll tell you something, I couldn't have even gone *in* a plane a couple of months ago, let alone jump *out* of one!"

"Well, I think that is really great!" exclaimed Fay, beaming at him. "I hope it goes really well for you. Now then, what about everyone else?" She looked at the young man sitting next to Pat. "John, how about you?"

One by one, each person in turn spoke aloud to the rest of the group; sharing with everyone all their failings and all their triumphs.

"I rode a bike today," someone said proudly.

"I smiled at a baby," said another.

No achievement was too small to mention, and no hurdle was thought to be too great to climb. Problems that seemed too vast and unbeatable when faced alone became so much smaller when shared with others who were experiencing the same things.

Here I felt safe. It didn't matter how much you panicked or how much you grieved – even frequent visits to the toilet could be made without embarrassment. Here, new friendships were made – all of us joined by a common bond – all of us caught up in the web of addiction.

"It's Heather, isn't it?" Marie turned her head around to look at me.

"That's right," I smiled at her.

"Are you still on drugs?" she asked me, her northern accent strong but not harsh.

"Yes – just 4 mg of Valium though. I've cut right down from 15 mg and I am just waiting to hear from the hospital so that I can come off altogether."

"So you were saying before. You're seeing Helen Carlisle then? I've heard quite a few people mention her – she's supposed to be very good."

"So I believe," I said. "I just wish the appointment would hurry up and come. Now I know the reason for feeling so ill I just want to come off as soon as possible."

"Are you going into hospital to do it?" she asked.

"No...I don't think so," I sounded unsure. "I would rather be at home if I could. You didn't go into hospital, did you?"

"No, I didn't," she slowly replied. "But then I did not really have any choice. My doctor had no idea what to do. It was he who told me to stop taking Valium – and so I did, just like that." She snapped her finger and thumb together.

"Isn't that dangerous?" I enquired, remembering what had happened to Connie.

"Yes it is. I know that now, but at that time I was totally naive."

"What actually happened to you?"

"I lost two days – they were completely blank," she spoke in a weary monotone. "And one of the first things I can remember was crawling to the mirror and getting the shock of my life – my hair was speckled with grey at the front. As all the muscles in my shoulders and neck had gone into spasm, I couldn't even lift my arm to brush it. It's still painful to move quickly." She put her hand to the back of her neck. "Mind you Fay is very good at massage. I find that really helps."

"When did all this happen?" I asked her.

"Three months ago," Marie replied.

"But you feel a bit better now though?" I sounded concerned.

"Good grief – yes!   I mean I couldn't even go out of the house before because my agoraphobia was so bad, and I had to have all the curtains closed because the light hurt my eyes."

"I find I have to wear sun-glasses now," I said.

"Yes, most of us do – it's very common. Noise as well – that was terrible." She paused and gave a chuckle. "We've got a pendulum clock in the lounge and Ken had to 'doctor' it."

"Doctor it?" I glanced questioningly at her husband.

"Yes, that's right," replied Ken. "I had to put a great big duster around the pendulum so she could not hear the ticking."

"It's true," she laughed. "Even the cat was not allowed to mew!" I smiled as she spoke, liking her sense of humour.

"Did your doctor know about all this?"

"Huh!" she snorted. "He had no idea whatsoever. All he said to me was, 'Get yourself to work Mrs Hall, it will do you the power of good.' I couldn't even walk at the time – never mind work!"

"My doctor is much nicer than that – but he's sceptical about the effects of drugs, too."

"Is he the one who is referring you to Dr. Carlisle?

"Yes, but I don't think he is very pleased."

"Look," she said, "I'd like to hear how you get on after you've been to see her. Will you let me know?"

"Sure," I replied. "I hope it will be soon though. I just want to get it over and done with!"

"Well, don't let my experiences put you off. I mean your withdrawal will be done properly under medical supervision, and of course you're half way there already."

But as we exchanged telephone numbers, just one thought ran through my mind. "It doesn't matter *how* much it will hurt or *how* hard it will be – I just want to get these drugs out of my body. I just want to be free!"

August 1983

"You'll be all right, just you wait and see," Pat's voice was strong and reassuring.

"I know, I have been telling her that all day," said Lou. But it seemed as though nothing was going to calm the awful fear that now ran havoc through my body, overpowering all other feelings.

Pat leaned against the doorway of the waiting-room in the Blackwell Unit. "Don't worry, Helen Carlisle will soon put you right," he said, smiling reassuringly. I looked across at him, he seemed so relaxed and confident.

"Have *you* been in to see her yet?" I asked quietly, sitting on my hands in order to stop them from shaking. The atmosphere in the room was heavy and suffocating, making me feel faint and sick. All I wanted to do was to run outside into the August sunshine.

"Yes," he replied, "and I haven't got to come back for a month, so that must be a good sign."

A young blonde nurse entered the room and looked over to Lou and I, smiling. "Right then, Heather, if you and your husband would like to come with me, I'll take you to see Dr. Carlisle."

"Good luck," Pat said, as we left the room.

"Thanks," smiled Lou with a nod.

"See you on Tuesday then?" he called, turning back as he walked to the main exit.

We walked with the nurse in the opposite direction to a room at the far end of the corridor. The door was open. Sunshine streamed onto a desk that faced the window and the white-coated figure seated there stood up to greet Lou and I, arm outstretched.

"Hello, I'm Doctor Carlisle," she said, shaking us both by the hand, "I'm so pleased to meet you." I noticed she was not very tall, her slim, youthful build belying her years. "Please, take a seat," she pointed to two chairs at the side of her desk, her smile, warm and genuine, immediately putting me at ease. As the fear, that had been so dominant before, began slowly to abate. my breathing became more regular. and I looked over at her as she sat down at her desk.

"I'm so sorry to have kept you waiting. I hope you didn't mind?" she turned sideways in her chair so she was facing us both. Her fair short hair, greying slightly at the temples, curled around gently tanned cheeks; lines of laughter – a legacy of fifty or more years of life – were etched into her features, and her eyes, blue and frank, beamed kindly from behind pale-framed spectacles.

"No. That's fine," I said with a thin smile. "It's just that I have a bit of a problem with agoraphobia at the moment."

"Of course – I quite understand," she replied, "this seems to be a problem shared by most of my patients." She picked up a letter that lay on her desk. "I see you have been seeing Dr. Meredith for about three years now and during this time you have been cutting down on Diazepam?"

"Yes – that's right."

"O.K." she spoke as she read, "and now you would like to come off the 4 mg that you are on at the moment? Dr. Meredith has asked me to arrange this."

I nodded eagerly, "Oh yes please. It's just that I have heard how much you have helped others with their withdrawal."

"Well," she said modestly, "I wouldn't say that – it's the patient that does all the work you know. I just guide them as best I can." She put the letter down and leaned back in her chair. "Now then," she said, "why don't you give me a general run-down on what has been happening to you since you have been on the drugs?"

Lou and I began to relate to her the story of my battle with tranquillisers, starting with the carefree early years, when the drugs, seeming to be the answer to all my problems, would calm, sedate or wipe out any worries or anxieties that came along, and leading up to the gradual decline, when eventually the fears, phobias and the constant ill-health came to dominate our lives.

"I do agree with you," she said when we had finished. "The amount of Diazepam that you are now on isn't doing you any good at all. I also think that you have been in withdrawal for quite some time: you see the Benzodiazepine type of tran- quilliser – Valium in your case – works by boosting up a natural chemical in the brain which calms you down, in order for you to relax and sleep. But once it has been taken for a long period – problems start to set in. You see, it is the *lack* of suppression that causes the withdrawal effects, and as tolerance to the drug builds up, these can even occur while you're still taking them. So you see, it is possible to take tranquillisers and suffer side- effects and withdrawal symptoms at the same time.

"So do you think this is what is happenimg to me?" I asked.

"I'm sure it is," she answered.

"And would increasing the dose keep the withdrawal at bay?"

"Yes – probably – that is until you became tolerant to that amount, too."

"Was that why when Dr. Dawson kept on prescribing different drugs for me to take with Valium that I used to feel so terrible when I stopped taking them?"

"Which ones were they?" she asked.

"Well...quite a few anti-depressants and sleeping pills – there was Tryptizol, Imipramine, Mogadon, Dalmane, Hemi- nevrin..." her eyes widened as I spoke, "and several others. Oh – and Ativan. I have been on that, on and off at night, for about three years now. I am not so bad when I've taken them, but the next day I feel dreadful!"

"You were more than likely going in and out of withdrawal, so it was hardly surprising that you were feeling ill." she explained. "You see you were giving your body a higher dose, so when you stopped taking them it would be screaming out for more..."

"What about the fear though, especially when I am left on my own? Is that a withdrawal symptom, too?"

"Nearly all the fears you have been experiencing are classic symptoms and are very common with most of my patients. But you will find that when you get through withdrawal they should disappear." She looked me up and down for a moment. "You look very pale, so there is a chance you could be anaemic. Have you had a recent blood-test?"

"Yes, Simon – Dr. Meredith – did one a few months ago."

"And do you know the result?"

"He said I was slightly anaemic."

"Right. So I think we'll have another one done just to see what it is now. What is your appetite like?"

"It's pretty poor at the moment. I wish I could eat a bit more because I'd like to put on weight!"

"I'm sure it will improve, so don't worry about that."

"How long does the withdrawal take?" I asked.

"Do you mean coming off the drugs or the actual time it takes to be symptom-free?"

"Both really."

"Well," she replied, "it depends on the withdrawal method you would like to use. You can do it slowly at home with regular visits to the unit – this way gives the least symptoms, but obviously they are more drawn out. Or you could choose a rapid withdrawal, which is usually done in hospital. This is a lot more acute, but gets it over and done with quickly – a bit like pulling off an elastoplast."

"How long would you have to stay in hospital?"

"Usually a couple of weeks or so."

I thought for a moment. "Well, I'd like to do it quickly, but at home if I can. Is that possible?"

"Well, first of all I must admit that I think that a rapid withdrawal would be best for you. You've been cutting down for far too long now, and with your present symptoms a slow process would just prolong the agony. But I am not sure if it is advisable for you to be at home." She looked over at Lou. "What do you think, Mr. Jones – would you be able to look after her?"

"Oh, yes – I think so," Lou nodded. "I mean I don't work at the moment, so there would be no problem there."

She thought for a little while. "Well, if you're sure," she said. "You will have to report nearly every day to the unit though. Will that be O.K?"

"No problem at all," Lou assured her. "I can bring her down in the car."She smiled at me. "What do you think, Heather? Are you happy with this arrangement?"

I nodded, the relief surging through me. "Oh, yes – I'd rather do it this way!" I said.

"Right," she picked up a pen and began to write on a piece of paper, "now this is what I want you to do. Let me see, today is Friday – so I want you to drop 1 mg each day until you get down to 1 mg, then drop $1/2$ mg for the last two days. That should take you up to Tuesday of next week, but I'd like to see you before then." She paused and thought for a moment. "Which would have to be at the weekend," she said frowning slightly. "I'll tell you what, I'll give you my number just in case of an emergency." She noticed my worried expression. "But don't worry, I'm sure there won't be one," she added with a reassuring smile.*

"We've got Fay's number as well," Lou told her.

"Good," she said, "I'm sure she will help if she can. I know she understands because she has gone through it herself. Anyway, it's just for the weekend." She handed me a piece of paper. "Now, here is the telephone number for you and I'd like to see you again on Monday, if that is O.K. You'll have to come to my department though, as there will be no clinic here."

As we stood up to leave, I felt an odd sense of excitement – a sort of nervous expectancy. Was this the turning point in my life? Was this the right road at last? The voice inside, so often unanswered and ignored, was quite definite this time. It said, "YES!"

I began to withdraw the remaining Valium immediately. There was no noticeable difference in any of the symptoms for

*We must remind readers that they should never attempt to undertake withdrawal of prescribed medicines without seeking medical advice.

two days – but on the third day my legs began to feel extremely wobbly and unsure.

"I can't walk in a straight line," I told Dr. Carlisle. It was Monday morning and we had reported to her as promised. "It's as though they are made of jelly and the floor is sloping upwards."

I was perched on a high stool in the middle of her office; even climbing onto that had proved difficult.

"Well, I think you are doing very well," she remarked with a smile. "Did you have any problems over the weekend at all?" I shook my head. "No...nothing really. Well maybe an increase in bowel spasms, but that's all."

"That's good," she replied, "so let me see, what are you down to at the moment?"

"Half a milligram," I said, "tomorrow will be my last day." I pulled my mouth into a mock grimace.

She looked pleased. "Well, if you do as well as you have been doing, I don't see any need for you to come here every day – unless, of course, you feel dramatically worse. What do you think?"

"If I have to come down will I have to telephone first?"

"Yes, you had better. Just ring Janet, my secretary, and she'll sort something out. I still want to see you soon though – so how about if we say same time on Friday?"

"Yes. That will be fine."

She watched as I climbed gingerly down off the stool. The floor beneath felt as though it had moved sideways – I was completely disorientated. "Poor Heather," she said gently. "Let's hope things don't get much worse for you. I'll keep my fingers crossed."

August 1983 – May 1984

Wednesday, August 23rd, 1983 was the first day of my new life – a life no longer supported by tranquillisers. Apart from the continual lack of balance and an increase in stomach and bowel cramps, I felt no different to the way I had felt while taking the tranquillisers.

"Maybe this is it!" I told myself. "It could be that with cutting them down for so long I've gone through most of the withdrawal." But two days later, on Friday evening, I realised I was wrong.

"What is the matter?" Lou asked with alarm. I had shot out of my chair and run across the floor to the door of the lounge.

"Please Lou – help!" I cried, covering my face with my hands.

"Heather, what is it?" He tried to put his arm around my shoulder.

"No-o!" I shouted pulling myself free. My heart had suddenly begun to pound loudly, banging against the walls of my chest, and a tremendous blind panic – the vastness of which I had never experienced before – was starting in the bottom of my stomach, turning everything over inside.

I made for the stairs, ran half way up, turned and ran back down again. I wanted to run away – to be free from my body.

"Please, help me!" I pleaded again. "Please, God help me!"

For a few moments, I seemed to lose all sense of recognition, "I don't know where I am; I don't know who I am!" I stretched my arm out to Lou. "Please, I'm so frightened."

"Come and sit down," he tried to guide me back to the lounge. "No! I can't. I want to go out!" I ran to the door.

"I'll come with you," he said patiently, "you can't go on your own." He took a hold of my hand and opened the door. The sun, now low in the sky, was still warm after the hot day. "Come on," he urged, "it's a lovely evening."

My whole body froze as I stepped outside. Fear ran rampant through every pore. "I can't, I can't! Please, I have to get back inside!"

Lou followed me as I hurried back into the house. "Come on, love. Try and relax if you can," his voice tried to hide his concern.

"I can't!" I explained frantically. "Everything has seized up inside." I wrapped my arms around my body, trying hard to ease the internal stiffness. "All my muscles hurt and my head feels like a balloon."

"Do you want me to ring Fay?" he asked in a worried voice. I nodded, these symptoms were bigger than any I had ever known – I needed help! I watched as he made the call, silently praying for this awful feeling to be taken away, begging for relief.

"She suggests that you have a deep warm bath," he said, putting the phone down. "That will help the muscles relax. Also if you can breathe into a paper bag this will help the panic." He walked over and gently put his arm around me. "Come on," he coaxed, "I'll help you upstairs."

As I climbed into the bath I looked at my body with horror. All my muscles had gone into spasm – the hard outline of them all, in my arms, legs and stomach, made me look like a body builder.

"What has happened to me?" I asked frantically.

"Don't worry," he reassured me, "Fay said this is a rebound action. The bath should help."

Gradually the warmth of the water began to take action. It soothed the taut muscles and calmed the pounding heartbeat. I began to feel safe and relaxed. It was in this bath – immersed up to my armpits in warm water – that I would spend many hours in the months to come.

Sleep never came that night. I climbed in and out of bed, pacing the floor up and down, not knowing where I wanted to be. My skin itched all over – as though there were hundreds of tiny creatures crawling underneath – and the muscles in my limbs jerked spasmodically. My head felt as though it was stuffed with cotton wool and any little light hurt my eyes. Everything was unreal – I was wrapped up in total fear – and I felt as though I was an alien in my own body.

The days that followed proved to be no better. Physical exertion of any kind brought on waves of weakness and panic. A simple task, like putting the kettle on, had to be done very slowly and carefully and any quick movement took my breath away, producing a feeling of faintness. Conversations – especially with people who did not understand about the drugs – were completely impossible: my heart would thud, perspiration would pour down my back, and my words would became slurred and difficult to pronounce. Everyday noises – such as the ticking of a clock, the sounds of children playing – jarred every nerve in my being, and sudden loud noises – a telephone ringing, a door slamming or a clatter of a plate – would reduce me to tears. Sleep no longer came with the night, and total exhaustion took over from fatigue. Many times, I thought it would be best to die.

"I hope things don't get any worse," I said to Simon. It was my first visit since the withdrawal from the drugs. This had been postponed for two weeks because of my increased agoraphobia. I had just been describing to him what had happened so far in my withdrawal.

He seemed very subdued and watched me closely as I spoke, his dark face clouded with scepticism. The bright sunlight that filled his room made it difficult for me to focus and I could hardly lift my head up to look at him, despite wearing dark glasses. Simon noticed my discomfort.

"Here, I'll close the blinds." He stood up and walked over to the window. I shrank down in my seat, weak and afraid, wishing I was back in the familiar security of my home.

"You know," the disapproval in his voice was obvious as he sat back down in his chair, "I made it clear in my letter to Dr. Carlisle that there was no way I wanted your existing symptoms exacerbated. It seems though, this is exactly what has happened."

"She's told me things will get better though," I returned. "Do you think that they will?"

"Well I hope so," he declared strongly, "because I don't like seeing you in this state."

I shivered in my seat. "Will I be able to carry on seeing you as well as Dr. Carlisle?"

He shook his head. "That wouldn't be very practical. It's probably best if you just stick to one doctor – that is until you are feeling a bit better. If you feel then that you need to come back and see me, Dr. Carlisle can refer you back."

I felt too ill to question this arrangement, I would sort that out at a later date. For now, I just wanted to go home.

"Right," my voice was hurried now, urgent even. "Can I go now, please?"

"Of course. Will you be alright? Is Lou with you?" he sounded concerned.

"Yes. He's just sitting outside in the car." Simon stood up and walked with me over to the door. "Well Heather, I do hope things soon improve for you. Come on," he beckoned with a grin, "I'll walk down with you. I want to make sure you get there in one piece."

*   *   *   *   *

The day after seeing Simon I had my first "window". Without any warning at all, the cotton wool feeling in my head disappeared. My eyes could focus, breathing became easy, and I no longer felt unreal. I looked out of the window – the grass looked greener, trees appeared taller – everything seemed sharp and bright. My body felt light and relaxed, my head completely clear. I felt normal! This feeling lasted for nearly two hours.

Later that day I made my daily phone call to Marie. "I felt O.K. this morning for a couple of hours," I told her.

"That's good," she said. "You will probably find you will feel like that more often now."

I had used the telephone a lot these last couple of weeks, it had been my life-line. It had kept me in touch with my many new friends from the group, each of us giving and receiving support to and from each other. Marion, Connie, Tina, Emily – these were all people who shared with me the problems of tranquilliser withdrawal – but it was Marie who I turned to during those blackest hours: slow-talking, dry-witted, Marie! It was she who, when there was no light at the end of the tunnel, gave me the hope to carry on. She was my rock.

The weeks passed by and I gradually became stronger. The change was so imperceptible at first, that I still had many days when I would do little but cry in despair. But it was the good days – the "windows" – that kept me going and, as Marie predicted, they became longer-lasting and more frequent.

As I regained physical strength, the psychological symptoms – my fear of going out or being on my own – gradually began to fade. The physiological symptoms – the bowel and stomach cramps – subsided and, as my appetite increased, I began to put on weight. The 'yellow' complexion I had had for so many years now disappeared, and the shine came back into my hair. I was starting to feel human once more.

I attended the support group and the Blackwell Unit regularly – it was at both these places that I felt most safe and at ease. I was fortunate in that I had found in Helen Carlisle a kind and caring doctor. Week by week, she would listen patiently and sympathetically to all my worries and complaints, constantly reassuring and supporting me, slowly but surely building up my confidence.

I was now becoming increasingly aware of everyday occurences – ones that had been covered over for so long by drugs. My mind was constantly asking questions about this new world – a world it had forgotton – and I could now *feel* again instead of being emotionally dead. Laughter had a proper place in my life once more. Very, very slowly I was returning to my old self.

JULIE'S STORY

June 1984

"I'm getting my driving licence back," Connie announced, sitting on the chair next to mine. It was a Wednesday afternoon and we had just finished our weekly aerobics class.

"Exercise helps to rid your body of all the toxins and helps to produce the right hormones in order to relax," Fay had said. So at one o'clock, every Wednesday afternoon, we would gather in the main room at Tranby Terrace, and (under the watchful eye of a trained instructor) we would thrash around like would-be gymnasts. Young, old, fat, thin – it was truly a remarkable sight!

"That's great," I said turning to Connie. "I bet you are pleased."

"Too true," she replied. "*I* knew it was the withdrawal from tranquillisers that caused the fit. They know that now, too!"

"It's terrible what these drugs have done to people," said a softly-spoken woman sitting opposite us. Her name was Marion; widowed at an early age and left to raise four sons on her own, her life had not been easy. She, like Connie and myself, had been off tranquillisers for just over a year now. We telephoned each other frequently: her gentleness and compassion made her a good and likeable friend.

Day sessions at Tranby Terrace were rarely busy – most people preferring the Tuesday evening meeting – and therefore there were no group-discussions. People more or less came as they pleased, dropping in for tea or coffee or maybe just a chat.

It was very much an open-house, some of us helping Fay with the running of the group. Tina and Connie did the typing or clerical work and sometimes I would give a hand with the telephone calls. Apart from existing clients needing reassurance and support, there were many new ones desperate for help. These were increasing in number, week by week.

So it was here at this informal little gathering, that we sat drinking tea and complaining good-naturedly to each other about aching muscles brought on by the aerobics.

"And how are you, Heather?" an elderly voice called from the far corner. This belonged to Emily, a small white-haired lady with the sweetest of smiles.

"Not so bad, thank you Emily," I replied. "How are you?"

"Oh, not too good at the moment," she said, "I'm getting a lot of bad days."

"Well, I think you are doing very well," I reassured her. She lived on her own and had been off tranquillisers for a couple of months now. She rang me often at home for reassurance and support, and I would try to help her as best as I could, remembering only too well my early days of withdrawal.

"Did you get all these pains in your stomach?" She asked me anxiously rubbing her hands across her middle.

"Yes," I said to her, "but they are a lot better now..."

As we spoke, the front door opened and a young girl of about twenty appeared. Fay, attending to some paper-work at the desk in the corner, stood up and greeted her. "Julie – how lovely!" She walked over and gave her a hug. "I must say you're looking great," she remarked, stepping back to admire her.

Fay was right. This pretty, pint-sized girl certainly did look great: her dark hair was cut short and her make-up was immaculately applied. A smart close fitting white suit with green accessories accentuated the slimness of her frame, and white stiletto-heeled shoes made her appear taller.

"What have you been doing with yourself?" asked Fay as she returned to her desk.

"Lots really," answered Julie. "I've just come back from a caravan holiday with my sister and her kids."

"Good," Fay replied encouragingly, "you like children, don't you? But how have *you* been? I hope you have been looking after yourself properly?" There was a hint of maternal concern in her voice.

Julie nodded her head. "Oh, I've been fine, I really have."

"Well, I'm pleased," beamed Fay, "and I know Dr. Carlisle will be as well!" She picked up some papers and carried them over to the inner door. "Connie, I am expecting a new client shortly. When she comes can you let me know, I'll be in the back office," and she disappeared through the door.

I turned to Julie. "Dr. Carlisle, she's your doctor?" this was more of a statement than a question.

"Yes, that's right," she nodded. Her smile, engaging but unsure, gave her a vulnerable look. I immediately warmed to her.

"She is nice, isn't she?" I commented.

"Oh, yes, she's lovely," she replied, "do you see her too?"

"Yes, she took me off tranquillisers ten months ago."

"Oh, I have only been off three months," she said. I noticed her voice – slightly husky in tone – had an intermittent 'tic'. Oddly enough this defect gave it a rather attractive quality.

"You look very well," I remarked.

"Oh, I feel O.K." she smiled. "Well – a lot better than I did anyway."

"Were you on tranquillisers very long? I mean you're not very old, are you?"

"I was given them when I was six," she told me. "I'm twenty now."

"Gosh, that's very young!" I exclaimed. "What on earth were you given them for?"

"I've got this 'tic'," she said, pointing to her throat. "It affects my speaking, you see. The doctors thought tranquillisers would help it."

"I see," I nodded. "It's not that noticeable though, is it?"

"Some days are worse than others," she answered. "It depends where I am and who I'm with. It's usually worse if I'm under stress or if I go out anywhere."

"Do you go out very often?" I asked her.

"Not really. You see I've been in hospital a lot over the years, then I had to go through the withdrawal. I'd like to go out now, but I don't know anyone to ask."

I thought for a few moments before speaking. I desperately wanted to help this girl. My mind flashed to Louise – naturally compassionate by nature – I was sure she would help her if she could.

"I've got a daughter just about your age," I said to her. "It's a shame you don't know one another..."

"I could get to know her," she cut in eagerly, "do you think she would go for a drink or something with me? I'm not bothered if it's only for an hour, just so I can say I have been out."

"I'm sure she will but I'll have to ask her first, of course. I tell you what, if you give me your telephone number I'll get her to ring you tonight."

*   *   *   *   *

Louise did agree to meet her – admittedly rather hesitantly at first – but Julie's natural warmth immediately won her over. They were soon close friends.

"I'm so pleased I met Louise," she told me. "She really understands, especially about withdrawal." She looked so happy sitting on the settee in our lounge; her 'tic' was barely noticeable.

"Well, she should," I said smiling at her, "she's had enough practice."

"Of course, she must have seen what happened to you. She's so easy to talk to. I feel as though I've known her for years."

I gave her a warm look. "Where are you going tonight?"

"Oh, just out for a drink, I think. Nothing special."

I was so pleased with the progress that Julie had made. Since meeting Louise she seemed to have gone forward in leaps and bounds. Even so, I still found it hard to believe that someone so young could have been prescribed so many different addictive drugs for so long. "Was it right, Julie, that you were first put on tranquillisers when you were just six years old?"

"Yes," she nodded, "my doctor put me on Serenace drops for my 'tic'."

"They're major tranquillisers aren't they? They're not Benzodiazepines."

"I think so."

"How long were you on these for?"

"Oh, quite a long time."

"And did they help your 'tic'?"

"No, not at all."

"But you were still prescribed them?"

"Yes. I had to go and see different doctors as well. But nobody seemed to know what was causing the 'tic'. In the end they admitted me to the Stanfield Unit for six weeks."

"I've never heard of that; where is it?"

"It's an annexe behind the new Stephenson Road Hospital – it's a sort of assessment clinic for people with behaviour disorders."

"Were you O.K. in there?"

"No! I hated it!" she declared emphatically. "There was one doctor in particular who will stay in my mind for ever," she scowled hard as she remembered, "Dr. Stephen Morrison – he was an arrogant, horrible man!"

"How do you mean?" I asked.

"Oh, it was just his attitude – cold and heartless. When I was admitted to the Winterton Hospital later on, he was there too."

"Winterton? isn't that the Psychiatric Hospital near North Hartley?"

"Yes," she replied, "I was in there for four and a half years."

"How old were you then?" I asked her.

"About twelve."

"Were you still on Serenace?"

"Oh, no. By this time the doctor had put me onto Librium."

"What about your 'tic' – was it still there?"

"Oh, yes," she nodded, "that never really went away."

"What sort of treatment did you have there?"

"Just more drugs," she shrugged, "Valium mainly, though sometimes they would put me on different ones."

I frowned across at her. "How many 'different ones' for goodness sake?"

She slowly blew out a low breath, and began to count on one hand. "Let me see now," she reflected, "apart from Valium, there was Largactil, Melleril, Phenobarbitone, Propanolol...oh, and many more – but I don't remember their names."

I shook my head in disbelief. "Did any of these help at all?"

"Not a bit," she answered, "they just seemed to irritate my 'tic' if anything. I remember one day, I was really depressed and I tried to put them down the toilet. The nurse saw me doing it and became very angry. When I still wouldn't take them, she hit me for being difficult."

"That's terrible!" I exclaimed, the indignation building up inside that a child should have to go through that sort of treatment.

"Yes, I know. Mind you I was very aggressive at the time."

"No wonder," I retorted, "anyone would be on all those tranquillisers. I know I was."

"I was very depressed as well," she continued, "in fact, I became suicidal."

"Well again," I explained, "as you know, those symptoms can be side-effects. Valium certainly made me like that."

"Dr. Morrison did not think that way though," Julie remarked vehemently. "He just kept on prescribing more pills. Honestly Heather, I really hated him – he was so cold and heartless." I noticed as she became more agitated, the more evident the 'tic' became.

"What did your parents think of all this?" I asked her. She could see I was concerned.

"They were not very happy at all," she replied. "They wanted to take me to see a private doctor, but Dr. Morrison got very annoyed about that and told them that he was the best in the area and if they took me out of the hospital too soon, I would never get better. He also said that he would make sure that no other doctor would ever take me on. It was dreadful Heather," she said, "they put me on to a points system: if I went out with my parents in the car and sat still, I would get extra points, but if I misbehaved, they were taken off."

My heart went out to this girl. "Poor Julie," I said, "it must have been awful for you. You were there for over four years as well, weren't you?"

"That's right," she nodded slowly. "Mind you in the end my mum and dad were so fed up that they did take me to see another doctor, privately this time."

"Who was that?"

"It was a Dr. Fisher from the Western General – he was the one who put me on to Ativan."

"You were on quite a high dose of that, weren't you?"

"Yes, I started off on the blue ones – 1 mg – then later on he 'upped' the dose to 2.5 mg – the yellow ones. I had to take them three times a day. I was walking about like a zombie! I still didn't feel any better, though. In fact things were worse than ever," she went on bitterly, "and I could hardly stand up! They made me do these humiliating and degrading tests as well. I had to drop ink onto blotting paper and things like that and they would watch my reactions from behind hidden cameras. I knew they were there though," she added with a laugh, "so I used to wave to them!"

"Was it around this time that you went to see Dr. Carlisle?" I asked.

"Yes, a Social Worker at the hospital told me about the support group in Tranby Terrace. My mum took me there and that is where I met Fay. It was she who told me about Helen Carlisle."

"You came off drugs in hospital, didn't you?"

"Yes, I was in for four weeks. Mind you," she added with a smile, "I didn't behave myself very well, when I was there. I don't think I was one of Dr. Carlisle's 'better patients'!"

"How do you mean?"

"Well, when they took the tranquillisers away, I just went crazy. I remember running up and down the ward screaming and shouting. I was so aggressive, I even attacked a nurse."

"Oh dear," I bit my bottom lip to suppress the amused smile. "Mind you, panic and violent outbursts can be part of withdrawal you know."

"Yes, I realise that now," she said. "The panic attacks were terrible. And big black depressions – I had a lot of those. I remember I could not even hold a knife and fork properly either – I couldn't get my hands to work. It was though there there was no use in the fingers."

"You were a lot better when you came out of hospital though, weren't you?"

"Oh, yes," her answer was definite, "mind you I couldn't have done it without Fay. She took me under her wing for a while. She was really marvellous."

I smiled across at her and her face, full of determination, smiled back. "Well, I think you're doing marvellously," I said, "especially when you consider how many drugs you have been taking over the years. I mean you were just a little girl when you were first given them, so really your body has never had a chance to work on its own. When you think about it, tranquillisers have controlled you for most of your life."

She nodded. "I know they have. This is what my mum says – she's very bitter about it now."

It was at that moment that Louise entered the room. She grinned warmly at Julie. "Sorry I have been so long," she said, "but I'm ready now."

"That's O.K.," answered Julie. "I've just been having a chat with your mum." I smiled at them both as they prepared to leave.

"Enjoy yourselves now," I said, "and watch what you are doing."

Louise cocked her head in my direction. "My mum still thinks I'm a little girl," she laughed.

"Yes I know," I grinned, "you probably always will be as well."

I watched as they walked out of the house, laughing and joking with each other. It was almost impossible to imagine how much Julie had come through and fought in her battle with addiction. Like the rest of us she had had years of her life suffocated under a blanket of tranquillisers, but for her the loss was especially acute – it represented the precious, formative years of her childhood and teens.

In the early days of withdrawal, many people think they are going mad. The world that emerges – a world not covered over by pills – can be a frightening place until the mind becomes used to its pictures and colours once more. For Julie, the world she found opening up before her was especially strange. The world she last remembered was seen through the eyes of a child – all her formative and adolescent years having been blocked out by tranquillisers. Somehow, during those drug-filled years she had grown-up – without any natural experience of the joys and sorrows of the process of growth – and now, without any preparation for the task, she had to face the world as an adult.

Coming to terms with this new person would be confusing, frightening and traumatic – and her journey of self-discovery was only just beginning. But Julie was a fighter and somehow I knew she would make it. She would come through in the end – 'tic' or no 'tic'.

September 1984

"Well I must say, you are looking much better than when I last saw you." Simon beamed at me with approval.

"I *feel* a lot better," I told him, settling down into my chair. I felt poised and confident. I had to be. I was on trial.

Thirteen months had now passed since I had stopped taking Valium and I had asked Dr. Carlisle if she could arrange for me to see Simon for one last time. "I'd like him to see for himself what progress I have made," I had said to her. "I'm sure he will see a difference." I had so much to tell him, so much I wanted him to know.

He stretched back in his chair, his chin resting on his crossed hands, the familiar long legs once more filling the space between us. I looked at him and he appeared, once again, relaxed and at ease. During my last two visits he had been so sceptical and disapproving of my course of action that the atmosphere between us had been awkward and tense. "This is more like the old Simon," I said to myself.

"Well come on then," he urged with a grin, "tell me what's been happening to you. You must have lots of news."

"Phew!" I rolled my eyes upwards in mock horror. "Where do you want me to start?"

"Well last time I saw you, you had only been off Valium for a couple of weeks. You were in a pretty bad state, if I remember rightly."

"That's true," I replied, grimacing at the painful memory. "I felt awful then. I thought I was never going to get better."

"How long were you like that?" he asked.

"Well...it's difficult to say," I reflected, "it was such a slow process at first. I remember though, just after seeing you the last time, everything became clear for a couple of hours – that was my first 'window'."

"First *'window'?*" he sounded puzzled.

"Yes, that's what we call them," I explained. "It's like an

opening of light into a dark room – a sort of feeling of normality."

He gave me a teasing smile. "Oh, I see," he chaffed, "and what did you see through your 'window'?"

"Now don't be like that," I chided him gently, "they were very important to me at the time."

"Oh, I'm sure they were," he said biting his bottom lip with feigned abashment. "I'm only joking with you!"

"Yes, I know that," I smiled. "Now do you want me to tell you about the 'window'?"

"Of course." The hint of amusement was still in his voice.

"Well, all of a sudden everything became clear and sharp. I was looking out of the window at the time and everything outside seemed bright and colourful – the trees and grass looked so green, my head felt normal, all the cotton-wool feeling had gone, and everything felt slow and calm inside. It was just as though a heavy pressure had been lifted off my body. At first it felt weird – because it was something I wasn't used to – but then I remembered that this was what I was like years ago, before I took the pills. I felt normal again. It only lasted about two hours and then just as quickly as it came, it disappeared. It was lovely while it lasted, though."

"A sort of taster of things to come?" smiled Simon.

"Yes, that's right. It kept me going when everything else looked black. A bit like a light at the end of the tunnel."

"So when this feeling passed over, did you go back to feeling like you did when I last saw you?"

"No, not really," I said, after a few moments' reflection. "I know I felt awful that day, I just wanted to go home."

"Yes – I remember. But you hadn't been off very long then, had you?"

"No – just a fortnight."

"You cut down the remaining Valium very quickly didn't you?"

"Yes, I came off over a weekend. Mind you Dr. Carlisle admits now, that that was a bit brutal. I think if I had gone to her later on she would have stretched it over a week or so. It's just that at that time I felt so low that I just wanted to get off them as quickly as possible. Anyway," I added, suddenly remembering his question, "the good days began to get closer together. I started to go out a lot more – nothing adventurous at first mind, just shopping in the town and things like that – but gradually, as I became more confident, we began to go out for a meal or away for the day in the car. I'm doing all sorts of things now – I've even made a film."

He opened his eyes wide in surprise. "Really! What sort of film?"

"Oh, it was a just a documentary about tranquillisers. It's been used in teaching hospitals and places like that."

"That's very good," he said with admiration. "Fame at last, eh?"

We both began to laugh. "I can think of easier ways to become famous," I joked.

"Even so," he continued, "you certainly couldn't have done that before, could you?"

"I *could* have done it before the tranquillisers took a hold of my mind. But I'm talking about ten years ago now."

"That's right, you always used to tell me that you had loads of confidence when you were younger," he nodded his head in agreement. "What about the fear of being left on your own? Is that any better? If I remember rightly, when Lou went out anywhere he used to have to get his mother or your friend, Eileen to look after you didn't he?"

"He has a good memory," I said to myself, thinking back to those drug-filled desperate days. It was hard to believe that they existed just over one year ago – they seemed to be a life-time away. "Yes, that's right, he did." I replied, "but I don't seem to mind any more. Sometimes, in fact I like being on my own. Mind you, I can still remember that fear. It was dreadful!"

"How about Lou? How is he coping now?"

"Well," I replied, "since we have been going to the group he's been a lot more understanding. Oh – and he's starting up his own business, so that must be good."

"So he didn't go back to his old job, then?"

"No, not after all this time. I think he preferred working for himself instead."

"Well, it's great that he's back at work – I'm really pleased about that. I bet you are too."

"Definitely," I nodded emphatically. "Mind you, when I was on tranquillisers, I used to think he would never work again. I was always so frightened."

"Do you think the tranquillisers gave you these fears then?"

"Oh, I'm sure they did. I'm not the only one either. Nearly everybody I know who has been addicted to them has had some form of fear."

"So what you're saying," he said thoughtfully, pursing his lips together, "is that all the fears you had were side-effects or withdrawal symptoms?"

I nodded my head again and stared at him, almost defiantly. "Yes, I do."

He looked solemn for a few moments, even a little sad. "Well, if that is true," he said, "and I'm beginning to think that it is, it makes me look like a complete duff."

"Oh, no," I broke in quickly. I had been ready for this. "That's not true. Honestly Simon, I couldn't have got through those three years if it hadn't been for you. I'm sure I *did* have problems that needed sorting out with psychotherapy – especially when I was cutting down on the pills. It was as though they had helped me to blot everything out. *You* remember my past, *you* know all those awful bits – well you helped me to come to terms with them. I can accept everything now."

A modest smile wiped the sadness from his face. "Well, I am glad I was of some help, even if it was just a little bit," he remarked sitting upright in his chair, crossing his legs one over the other. "But tell me – how are you *now?* I can see you *look* a lot better, but how do you *feel?*"

"Well, much better mentally," I told him. "Physically? Well...my body still needs a lot of building up. I mean, it was fed on drugs for so many years, it's bound to be run down. Dr. Carlisle gave me a course of iron injections for anaemia, so that helped a bit. Oh – yes, and she also arranged physiotherapy for me, to have breathing exercises."

"Breathing exercises?"

"Yes. Apparently hyperventillation is a very common symptom in withdrawal, because the respiratory muscles have been controlled by drugs for so long that they have forgotten how to work properly: you have to teach them *how* again."

"I see," he said, raising his eyebrows. "You seem very genned up on all this."

"Well, I like to know what and why things happen; I always have." I replied with a smile.

"That's right. I should have remembered that," Simon grinned back. "But how are you sleeping now? The last time I saw you, you were getting hardly any at all."

"Not too bad now," I replied. "I still get a lot of colic at night, though, which tends to keep me awake."

"But if it wasn't for that, would you be able to sleep?"

"Oh, yes, no problem. I did suffer from palpitations and a fast heart-beat for a while, which also kept me awake. But these have calmed right down now."

He smiled at me approvingly. "Well, I must say, you seem to be doing very well indeed. You wouldn't think you were the same person that I met all those years ago." Then he paused and took a deep breath. "Mind you – if side-effects and withdrawal from tranquillisers do cause all these problems, it's about time we doctors prescribed them with a little more caution."

"I'm glad you think like that," I said. "I was concerned that you might have thought otherwise."

"Well, I can't really, can I?" he answered. "Not after seeing you now. I must admit, I took a lot of convincing – but," he looked me up and down, "the evidence is impossible to ignore."

"Well, I feel different," I told him, "it's like being re-born. Mind you, I still can't cope with stress very well. Dr. Carlisle says this is because tranquillisers prevent the natural chemical which helps you cope with stress from being produced; it can take some time before the body produces it again. This is why it can take two years – or even longer – to be free from the symptoms of withdrawal."

Simon let out a breath. "As long as that?" He sounded surprised.

"Well...that doesn't mean you will feel terrible for that long – you're improving all the time really. No, what I think she means is that it can take that long to be totally symptom-free. Mind you, I do know of people who have hardly any symptoms at all after only a few months, so I suppose everyone is different."

"Well, maybe so," Simon agreed, "but I'm so pleased for *you!* You've done really well."

"Thank you." I warmed to his praise. "I've a long way to go yet though."

"Well Heather, I'm sure you'll make it; let's face it, you have come a long way to get this far already."

"Well, I hope so." I smiled affectionately at him, realising that now was the time to take my leave. I had achieved what I had set out to do – Simon believed in what I had said and had given me his full approval – that was the most important thing.

As I stood up and glanced at this gentle-voiced young man with the quiet eyes I felt a surge of apprehension. Here was someone who knew my mind better than I did myself, who had fed and nurtured my sanity for over three years, as both advisor and confessor. He had cured me of all the bitterness and resentments of my youth; walked with me through the depths of my despair; watched patiently and protectively as I came to terms with the problems in my life and, finally, come to share in the joy of my triumph over addiction.

I had bared my inner-most thoughts and soul to this man, he knew all my faults and weaknesses. He was, in some senses, an extension of myself – and here I was saying farewell to him for the last time. This feeling of loss made sense: in a way, I was losing a part of myself.

But although it was with a mixture of sadness and uneasiness that I said goodbye to Simon and walked down the stairs towards the main exit of the hospital, it was another sensation that filled my heart as I stepped outside into the autumn sunlight, one of peculiar light-headedness and freedom – as though I had just been released from prison. The world that had newly emerged in my perceptions was no longer shrouded by pills and I knew it to be wonderfuly full and alive. True, the road ahead was not going to be completely smooth – this had been the hardest task of my life and it wasn't over yet – but I also knew Simon was right: I had come this far, I would make it!

I smiled at Lou as I climbed into the car.

"Is everything all right love?" he asked.

"Yes," I nodded, "everything's all right."

And somehow I knew it was going to be.